Ten Paintings by Paul Cézanne
formerly in the Auguste Pellerin Collection

Ten Paintings by Paul Cézanne formerly in the Auguste Pellerin Collection

Sale 7075

Auction: Thursday, November 13, 1997 at 7 pm

Absentee Bids
This catalogue may be referred to as 7075 "PELLERIN"
Fax for bids only: (212) 606-7016

Admission to Evening Sale by Ticket Only
For Tickets, please call (212) 606-7171
Written requests should be directed to
Special Sales Department, Attention: TICKETS

Exhibition

Friday, November 7
1 pm to 5 pm

Saturday, November 8
10 am to 5 pm

Sunday, November 9
1 pm to 5 pm

Monday, November 10
10 am to 5 pm

Tuesday, November 11
10 am to 5 pm

Wednesday, November 12
10 am to noon

Catalogue

$23 at the gallery, $29 by mail,
$37 overseas

Front Cover Illustration: Lot 112

William F. Ruprecht, Principal Auctioneer,
License No. 0794917

SOTHEBY'S

1334 York Avenue (at 72nd Street) New York, NY 10021
Telephone: (212) 606-7000

International Impressionist and Modern Art Department

Simon de Pury
Chairman, Europe

Michel Strauss
Senior Expert
Impressionist and Modern Art
Europe

John Tancock
Senior Expert
Impressionist and Modern Art
North America and Japan

NEW YORK
Alexander Apsis *(Director)*
Laurel Beckett
Stephane Cosman Connery
Blake Koh
David Norman
Lilly Phipps
(212) 606 7360

BERLIN
Lucy Dew
(4930) 204 4119

BEVERLY HILLS
Victoria Edwards
(310) 274 0340

BRUSSELS
Monique Bréhier
(322) 648 00 80

CHICAGO
Helyn Goldenberg
(312) 664 6800

COLOGNE
Ursula Niggemann
(49221) 257 4956

FRANKFURT
Nina Buhne
(4969) 74 0787

GENEVA
Daniella Luxembourg
Caroline Lang
(4122) 732 85 85

MADRID
Wendy Loges
(341) 522 2902

LONDON
Melanie Clore *(Director)*
Philip Hook
Adrian Biddell
Helena Newman
David Breuer-Weil
Oliver Barker
Lavinia Calza
(44 171)408 5393

MILAN
Claudia Dwek
(392) 29 500 1

PARIS
Andrew Strauss
Emmanuel Di-Donna
(331) 53 05 53 05

SEOUL
Howard Rutkowski
82 (2) 733 5733

STOCKHOLM
Hans Dyhlên
(468) 679 5478

TEL AVIV
Rivka Saker
Daniella Luxembourg
David Breuer-Weil
(9723) 522 3822

TOKYO
John Tancock
(813) 3230 2755

VIENNA
Dr. Agnes Husslein
(43222) 512 4772

ZURICH
Daniella Luxembourg
(411) 202 0011

Sale Inquiries

Specialists In Charge

Alexander Apsis
Laurel Beckett
David Norman
(212) 606 7360
Fax (212) 606 7037

Client Liasion
Raul Suarez
(212) 606 7360

Client Advisory Services

*For assistance in buying at
this auction*
Roberta Louckx (212) 606 7415
Mallory Hathaway (212) 606 7447
Geraldine Nager Griffin (212) 606 7568
Fax (212) 606 7269

Asian Client Relations
Jean Kim (212) 606 7257
Natsuko Hidaka (212) 606 7427
Fax (212) 606 7269

Absentee Bids

Frederica Lauder (212) 606 7414
Fax (212) 606 7016

Client Services Desk

(212) 606 7116

24 Hour Recorded Information

Sales Results
(212) 606 7901

Current auctions and exhibitions
(212) 606 7909

Payment and Shipping

Buying
Mary Stuhr (212) 606 7471
Fax (212) 606 7043

Shipping
Molly Ott (212) 606 7411
Lexie Forman (212) 606 7510
Fax (212) 606 7013

Selling
Andrea Katz (212) 606 7298
Fax (212) 606 7044

Subscriptions

(800) 444 3709 From within the U.S.
(203) 847 0465 From outside the U.S.

Sotheby's World Wide Web Site:

http://www.sothebys.com

Conditions of Sale

The following Conditions of Sale and Terms of Guarantee are Sotheby's, Inc. and the Consignor's entire agreement with the purchaser relative to the property listed in this catalogue.

The Conditions of Sale, Terms of Guarantee, the glossary, if any, and all other contents of this catalogue are subject to amendment by us by the posting of notices or by oral announcements made during the sale. The property will be offered by us as agent for the Consignor, unless the catalogue indicates otherwise. By participating in any sale, you acknowledge that you are bound by these terms and conditions.

1 Goods auctioned are often of some age. The authenticity of the Authorship of property listed in the catalogue is guaranteed as stated in the Terms of Guarantee and except for the Limited Warranty contained therein, all property is sold "AS IS" without any representations or warranties by us or the Consignor as to merchantability, fitness for a particular purpose, the correctness of the catalogue or other description of the physical condition, size, quality, rarity, importance, medium, provenance, exhibitions, literature or historical relevance of any property and no statement anywhere, whether oral or written, whether made in the catalogue, an advertisement, a bill of sale, a salesroom posting or announcement, or elsewhere, shall be deemed such a warranty, representation or assumption of liability. We and the Consignor make no representations and warranties, express or implied, as to whether the purchaser acquires any copyrights, including but not limited to, any reproduction rights in any property. We and the Consignor are not responsible for errors and omissions in the catalogue, glossary, or any supplemental material.

2 Prospective bidders should inspect the property before bidding to determine its condition, size, and whether or not it has been repaired or restored.

3 A buyer's premium will be added to the successful bid price and is payable by the purchaser as part of the total purchase price. The buyer's premium is 15% of the successful bid price up to and including $50,000, and 10% on any amount in excess of $50,000.

4 We reserve the right to withdraw any property before the sale and shall have no liability whatsoever for such withdrawal.

5 Unless otherwise announced by the auctioneer, all bids are per lot as numbered in the catalogue.

6 We reserve the right to reject any bid. The highest bidder acknowledged by the auctioneer will be the purchaser. In the event of any dispute between bidders, or in the event of doubt on our part as to the validity of any bid, the auctioneer will have the final discretion to determine the successful bidder, cancel the sale, or to reoffer and resell the article in dispute. If any dispute arises after the sale, our sale record is conclusive. Although in our discretion we will execute order or absentee bids or accept telephone bids as a convenience to clients who are not present at auctions, we are not responsible for any errors or omissions in connection therewith.

7 If the auctioneer decides that any opening bid is below the reserve of the article offered, he may reject the same and withdraw the article from sale, and if, having acknowledged an opening bid, he decides that any advance thereafter is insufficient, he may reject the advance.

8 Subject to fulfillment of all of the conditions set forth herein, on the fall of the auctioneer's hammer, title to the offered lot will pass to the highest bidder acknowledged by the auctioneer, and such bidder thereupon (a) assumes full risk and responsibility therefor (including, without limitation, liability for or damage to frames or glass covering prints, paintings or other works), and (b) will immediately pay the full purchase price or such part as we may require. In addition to other remedies available to us by law, we reserve the right to impose from the date of sale a late charge of 1½% per month of the total purchase price if payment is not made in accordance with the conditions set forth herein. All property must be removed from our premises by the purchaser at his expense not later than 10 business days following its sale and, if it is not so removed, (i) a handling charge of 1% of the total purchase price per month from the tenth day after the sale until its removal will be payable to us by the purchaser, with a minimum of 5% of the total purchase price for any property not so removed within 60 days after the sale, and (ii) we may send the purchased property to a public warehouse for the account, at the risk and expense of the purchaser.

If any applicable conditions herein are not complied with by the purchaser, the purchaser will be in default and in addition to any and all other remedies available to us and the Consignor by law, including, without limitation, the right to hold the purchaser liable for the total purchase price, including all fees, charges and expenses more fully set forth herein, we, at our option, may (x) cancel the sale of that, or any other lot or lots sold to the defaulting purchaser at the same or any other auction, retaining as liquidated damages all payments made by the purchaser, or (y) resell the purchased property, whether at public auction or by private sale, or (z) effect any combination thereof. In any case, the purchaser will be liable for any deficiency, any and all costs, handling charges, late charges, expenses of both sales, our commissions on both sales at our regular rates, legal fees and expenses, collection fees and incidental damages. We may, in our sole discretion, apply any pro-

ceeds of sale then due or thereafter becoming due to the purchaser from us or any affiliated company, or any payment made by the purchaser to us or any affiliated company, whether or not intended to reduce the purchaser's obligations with respect to the unpaid lot or lots, to the deficiency and any other amounts due to us or any affiliated companies. In addition, a defaulting purchaser will be deemed to have granted and assigned to us and our affiliated companies, a continuing security interest of first priority in any property or money of or owing to such purchaser in our possession or in the possession of any of our affiliated companies, and we may retain and apply such property or money as collateral security for the obligations due to us or to any affiliated company of ours. We shall have all of the rights accorded a secured party under the New York Uniform Commercial Code. Payment will not be deemed to have been made in full until we have collected good funds. In the event the purchaser fails to pay any or all of the total purchase price for any lot and Sotheby's nonetheless elects to pay the Consignor any portion of the sale proceeds, the purchaser acknowledges that Sotheby's shall have all of the rights of the Consignor to pursue the purchaser for any amounts paid to the Consignor, whether at law, in equity, or under these Conditions of Sale.

9 **All lots in this catalogue are offered subject to a reserve, which is the confidential minimum price acceptable to the Consignor.** No reserve will exceed the low presale estimate stated in the catalogue, or as amended by oral or posted notices. We may implement such reserve by opening the bidding on behalf of the Consignor and may bid up to the amount of the reserve, by placing successive or consecutive bids for a lot, or bids in response to other bidders. In instances where we have an interest in the lot other than our commission, we may bid up to the reserve to protect such interest. In certain instances, the Consignor may pay us less than the standard commission rate where a lot is "bought-in" to protect its reserve.

10 Unless exempted by law, the purchaser will be required to pay the combined New York State and local sales tax, any applicable compensating use tax of another state, and if applicable, any federal luxury or other tax, on the total purchase price. The rate of such combined tax is 8¼% in New York City and ranges from 4% to 8½% elsewhere in New York.

11 These Conditions of Sale and Terms of Guarantee, as well as the purchaser's and our respective rights and obligations hereunder, shall be governed by and construed and enforced in accordance with the laws of the State of New York. By bidding at an auction, whether present in person or by agent, order bid, telephone or other means, the purchaser shall be deemed to have consented to the jurisdiction of the state courts of, and the federal courts sitting in, the State of New York.

12 We are not responsible for the acts or omissions in our packing or shipping of purchased lots or of other carriers or packers of purchased lots, whether or not recommended by us. Packing and handling of purchased lots is at the entire risk of the purchaser. If we obtain on behalf of the purchaser an export license for an item containing an endangered species, there will be a charge of $150 for each license obtained.

13 In no event will our liability to a purchaser exceed the purchase price actually paid.

14 Sotheby's has guaranteed a minimum price to the consignor for all property in this sale.

Terms of Guarantee

Sotheby's warrants the authenticity of Authorship of each lot contained in this catalogue on the terms and conditions set forth below.

1 *Definition of Authorship.* "Authorship" is defined as the creator, period, culture, source of origin, as the case may be, as set forth in the **BOLD TYPE HEADING** of a lot in this catalogue, as amended by any oral or written salesroom notices or announcements. **If there is a "Glossary" of terms in this catalogue, please note that any such heading represents a qualified statement or opinion and is not subject to these Terms of Guarantee.** Sotheby's makes no warranties whatsoever, whether express or implied, with respect to any material in the catalogue, other than that appearing in **BOLD TYPE HEADING** and subject to the exclusions in 5 and 6 below.

2 *Guarantee Coverage.* Subject to the exclusions in 5 and 6 below, Sotheby's warrants the Authorship (as defined above) of a lot for a period of five years from the date of sale of such lot and only to the original purchaser of record at the auction. If it is determined to Sotheby's satisfaction that the **BOLD TYPE HEADING** is incorrect, the sale will be rescinded as set forth in 3 and 4 below, provided the lot is returned to Sotheby's at the original selling location in the same condition in which it was at the time of sale. It is Sotheby's general policy, and Sotheby's shall have the right to have the purchaser obtain, at the purchaser's expense, the opinion of two recognized experts in the field, mutually acceptable to Sotheby's and the purchaser, before Sotheby's determines whether to rescind a sale under the above warranty. If the purchaser requests, Sotheby's will provide the purchaser with the names of experts acceptable to it.

3 *Non-Assignability.* The benefits of this warranty are not assignable and shall be applicable only to the original purchaser of record and not to any subsequent owners (including, without limitation, heirs, successors, beneficiaries or assigns) who have, or may acquire, an interest in any purchased property.

4 *Sole Remedy.* It is specifically understood and agreed that the rescission of a sale and the refund of the original purchase price paid (the successful bid price, plus the buyer's premium) is exclusive and in lieu of any other remedy which might otherwise be available as a matter of law, or in equity. Sotheby's and the Consignor shall not be liable for any incidental or consequential damages incurred or claimed.

5 *Exclusions.* This warranty does not apply to: (i) Authorship of any paintings, drawings or sculpture created prior to 1870, unless the lot is determined to be a counterfeit (a modern forgery intended to deceive) which has a value at the date of the claim for rescission which is materially less than the purchase price paid for the lot; or (ii) any catalogue description where it was specifically mentioned that there is a conflict of specialist opinion on the Authorship of a lot; or (iii) Authorship which on the date of sale was in accordance with the then generally accepted opinion of scholars and specialists; or (iv) the identification of periods or dates of execution which may be proven inaccurate by means of scientific processes not generally accepted for use until after publication of the catalogue, or which were unreasonably expensive or impractical to use.

6 *Limited Warranty.* As stated in paragraph 1 of the Conditions of Sale, neither Sotheby's nor the Consignor makes any express or implied representations or warranties whatsoever concerning any property in the catalogue, including without limitation, any warranty of merchantability or fitness for a particular purpose, except as specifically provided herein.

Important Notice

Bidding privileges for this sale will only be granted to purchasers who have pre-registered with our Accounting Department at least three days prior to the sale. Please contact Mary Stuhr (212) 606-7471 if you wish to arrange for a paddle.

Auguste Pellerin

Auguste Pellerin (1852-1929) was one of the greatest collectors of the late nineteenth and early twentieth centuries. Known above all through his collections, his personality and motivation yet remain relatively obscure. How was it, for example, that the manufacturer of margarine who established factories in France, Germany, England and Scandinavia, who later became Norwegian consul-general in Paris (1906-1924) assembled a collection of Cézanne's work that at one time might have numbered 150 or more works? The recently published catalogue raisonné by John Rewald lists the Pellerin provenance in over 150 works, approximately one sixth of the total number of 954. A study of the pattern of Pellerin's collecting activities reveals that he had no interest whatsoever in assembling a well-balanced, heterogeneous collection of works by various artists. He collected the work of particular artists in depth, not to say obsessively, only to rid himself of unwanted canvases when his taste changed and developed. Like so many other great collectors, the Havemeyers for example, Pellerin began by collecting art that was currently fashionable. The German art historian Emil Waldman described how Auguste Pellerin "...who today owns Cézannes, some one hundred of them, began with [Jean-Jacques] Henner in the days when he had just established his margarine factories in Scandinavia, France, Germany and England. He soon got rid of these; once he had come across Corot, no substitute would do. But even Corot had to go after Pellerin had seen the Impressionists. Then, a few years later, he gave them up and only stuck with Manet. And after Manet had been enshrined for some time as the sole ruler in the house at Neuilly, he too had to leave and his rival moved in. Thus the road of one of the greatest modern collectors led from Henner to Cézanne.

When Mr. Pellerin sold his Henners and Vollons in favor of Corots, his friends were surprised. They felt that he was rich enough to keep Henner and Vollon. Yet, he didn't keep them; his aim was not to found a museum but to live with his pictures. "His" painter, in those days, was Corot, just as today "his" painter is Cézanne. The people who once advised him to keep Henner had no passion for art and did not understand the true nature of the collector; they were unaware of the main feature of the modern collection; the one-sidedness." (E. Waldmann, Sammler und ihresgleichen, Berlin, 1920, p. 33)

Although Pellerin owned outstanding paintings by the Impressionists- for example Camille au Jardin avec Jean et sa Bonne, 1873 (Bührle collection, Zurich) and Le Pont d'Argenteuil, 1874 (Bayerische Stadtsgemäldesammlungen, Munich) by Monet and L'Inondation à Port Marly, 1876 by Sisley (Musée d'Orsay)- the artists he collected in depth were Manet and Cézanne. Among the more than fifty paintings and pastels (as well as numerous works on paper) by Manet owned by Pellerin were some of the greatest. He owned Le Déjeuner dans l'Atelier, 1868 (Bayerische Stadtsgemäldesammlungen, Munich), La

The Pellerin residence in Neuilly, circa *1925. Lot 113 is over the mirror to the left.*

Serveuse de Bocks, 1879 (Musée d'Orsay, Paris) as well as Le Bar aux Folies-Bergères, 1881-82 (Courtauld Institute, London) and was still making significant purchases at the time when he began buying his first Cézannes. Although he gradually sold his holdings of Manet, as late as 1910 Bernheim-Jeune held an exhibition of thirty-five pieces by Manet, all of which came from the Pellerin collection.

Gradually, however, Cézanne took over and he made his first purchases in the late 1890s, a time when his work was known only to a few artists such as Renoir and Pissarro (see Lots 111 and 115) and writers and enlightened collectors such as Victor Chocquet and Dr. Paul Gachet. In December 1898 he purchased his first Cézanne from Ambroise Vollard who had given the artist his first one-man show in 1895. Six months later he attended the Victor Chocquet estate sale held at Galerie Georges Petit on July 1, 1899 and purchased Le Clos Normand (Hattenville) (Rewald 507) for 750 francs. Thereafter followed regular purchases not only from

Vollard but from Bernheim-Jeune and Jos Hessel. Bernheim-Jeune became one of the principal sources. On July 7, 1904, for example, he purchased seven important paintings from Bernheim-Jeune including Les Joueurs de Cartes (Rewald 710); Femme à la Cafetière (Rewald 781); Madame Cézanne au Fauteuil (Rewald 655); Jeune Italienne Accoudé (Rewald 812). Not limiting his purchases to

The Pellerin residence in Neuilly, circa 1925. Lot 111 is the bottom right painting on the left hand wall.

dealers, Pellerin also attended the important auctions, acquiring six of the nine Cézannes in the Emile Zola estate sale on March 9, 1903. This last documented purchase for a Cézanne was at the Gangnat sale in 1925 when he paid the record price of 528,000 francs for Grand Pin et Terres Rouges (Bellevue) (Rewald 537).

By the early years of this century the significance of Pellerin's holdings of Cézanne's work had become apparent. At the great Cézanne retrospective held at the Salon d'Automne in 1907, 25 of the paintings exhibited came from the Pellerin collection. Upon proper recommendation Pellerin would also allow visitors to view the collection in his house at Neuilly. Among these was Roger Fry who in the preface to the first edition of his monograph published in 1927 stated that "M. Pellerin's collection is so much the most representative of all the various phases of Cézanne's art in existence, that a study of it is essential to his development."

Seventy years later this is more than ever apparent. Extensive as it was, the collection was well balanced, representing all phases of Cézanne's development and including not only some of his greatest masterpieces- for example

Portrait du Peintre Achille Emperaire (Rewald 139- Musée d'Orsay), Les Joueurs de Cartes (Rewald 706- Metropolitan Museum of Art, New York) and Femme à la Cafetière (Rewald 781- Musée d'Orsay, Paris)- but also quantities of difficult, experimental works. In fact Pellerin seems to have held the early, expressionist work in particular esteem and a good third of the paintings in his collection dated from this period. At a time when even Cézanne's greatest admirers found the early work problematic his enthusiasm was noteworthy.

In 1907, for example, Louis Granel who had just purchased the Jas de Bouffan offered to have Cézanne's decorative panel, for the Jas de Bouffan, Les Quatre Saisons, 1860-61 detached

The Pellerin residence in Neuilly, circa *1925. Lot 106 is the upper painting on the extreme left; Lot 110 is on the lower left and lot 109 is on the bottom center of the right hand wall.*

from the wall and presented to the state. The offer was refused. Writing about this incident, Germain Bazin observed that " For the sake of Cézanne's Impressionist masterpieces, one could reject, at that time, the work he did before 1870. There was no-one but Auguste Pellerin to understand it." (Germain Bazin, Impressionist Painting in the Louvre, London, 1961, p. 50). Referring to Pellerin's holdings of work from Cézanne's first period, Sylvie Patin stressed "The harmonious way in which Pellerin built up his collection, not only as a whole but in the balance between the painter's various themes: eleven portraits, thirteen miscellaneous figure compositions, five landscapes, one still life, one interior. Among the portraits were two Portraits of the Artist {including Lot 107} Portrait of Louis Auguste Cézanne, Father of the Artist reading 'L'Événement', four

Portraits of Uncle Dominique {including Lot 108} and finally the celebrated Achille Emperaire which was rejected at the 1870 Salon. Among the figure compositions were the Christ in Limbo from the drawing-room at Jas de Bouffan, The Preparation for the Funeral {Lot 113}, A Modern Olympia {Lot 112}, The Orgy, Le Déjeuner sur l'herbe, Marion and Valabrègue setting out for the Motif, The Walk {Lot 114}, Paul Alexis reading at Zola's House and the lovely Pastoral (Idyll). Among the landscapes were The Fishing Village at L'Estaque, Melting Snow at L'Estaque, and Paris: Quai de Bercy {Lot 115}. The still life was Sugarpot, Pears and Blue Cup." (Sylvie Patin, "The Collectors of Cézanne's Early Works" in , *Cézanne the Early Years 1859-1872*, exhibition catalog, London, 1988, p. 60).

Upon Pellerin's death in 1929 he bequested three particularly fine still-lifes to the Louvre- Nature Morte à la Soupière, 1877 (Rewald 302), La Table de

The Pellerin residence in Neuilly, circa 1925. Lots 114 and 115 are visible on the right hand wall.

Cuisine (Nature Morte au Panier), 1888-90 (Rewald 636) and Nature Morte aux Oignons, 1896-98 (Rewald 803)- all since transfered to the Musèe d'Orsay. To mark the fiftieth anniversary of Cézanne's death in 1906, M. and Mme Jean-Victor Pellerin donated Femme à la Cafetière, *circa* 1895 to the Louvre. Further donations to the Louvre included Portrait de Peintre Achille Emperaire, 1867-68 (Rewald 139) in 1964, Mont Saint-Victoire, circa 1890 (Rewald 698) and Portrait de Gustave Geffroy, 1895-96 (Rewald 791) and a group of twelve pictures in 1982.

Ten Paintings by Paul Cézanne formerly in the Auguste Pellerin Collection

Lots 106-115

Thursday

November 13

1997

7 pm

106 Paul Cézanne (1839-1906)

PORTRAIT DE VICTOR CHOCQUET

Oil on canvas
7 by 5 in. 20 by 15 cm.

Painted *circa* 1880.

$300,000–400,000

Paul Cézanne, *Victor Chocquet assis*, c. 1877
Oil on canvas Columbus Museum of Art,
Ohio; Museum Purchase: Howald Fund

Victor Chocquet is widely recognized to have been one of the most remarkable collectors of the latter half of the 19th century, a man of modest means who nevertheless managed to assemble a distinguished collection of paintings, drawings, furniture, silver and porcelain dispersed after his death at Galerie Georges Petit, July 1, 3-4, 1899. Born in Lille in 1821, he was working for the customs administration in Paris when he married in 1857. His first enthusiasm was for the work of Delacroix, a passion that he shared with the two artists who were shortly to become among his closest friends, Renoir and Cézanne. Renoir took Chocquet to the gallery of Père Tanguy in the fall of 1875 where he made his first purchase of a Cézanne, *Trois baigneuses*, 1874-75 (Rewald 258-Musée d' Orsay, Paris). Difficult and temperamental as he was, Cézanne had considerable affection and respect for Chocquet, permitting him to assist in the selection of the fourteen canvases that were shown at the third Impressionist Exhibition in April 1877. Several of the works actually belonged to Chocquet, including the first portrait Cézanne painted of him (Rewald 292: Private Collection, New York). He was eventually to own some thirty-five paintings by Cézanne.

Chocquet's devotion to the cause of the Impressionists became apparent in 1877 when, having resigned from his customs post early in the year, he was able to spend all his time at the third Impressionist Exhibition, defending the works of the artists in person. Georges Rivière described him in action: "He [Chocquet] was something to see, standing up to hostile crowds at the exhibition during the first years of Impressionism. He accosted those who laughed, making them ashamed of their unkind comments, lashing them with ironic remarks ...Hardly had he left one group before he would be found, farther along, leading a reluctant connoisseur, almost by force, up to canvases by Renoir, Monet, or Cézanne, doing his utmost to make the man share his admiration for these reviled artists ...He exerted himself tirelessly without ever departing from that refined courtesy that made him the most charming, and the most dangerous, adversary."(Quoted in Anne Distel, *Impressionism: The First Collectors*, New York, 1990, p. 137)

106 *(actual size)*

Paul Cézanne, *Victor Chocquet (1821-1891)*, c. 1877. Oil on canvas, *13 ⅞ by 10 ¼ in.* Virginia Museum of Fine Arts, Richmond, Virginia. Collection of Mr. and Mrs. Paul Mellon. Photo: Grace Wen Hwa Ts'ao. © 1997 Virginia Museum of Fine Arts

The inheritance of the estate of Mme. Chocquet's mother in 1882 enabled the couple to move to Normandy. Cézanne made several visits to one of the properties they owned at Hattenville where he painted a number of landscapes and his last portrait of Chocquet. Chocquet died in 1891.

Cézanne painted six portraits of the collector whom John Rewald characterized as "certainly the first consistent buyer and champion of Cézanne's work as well as his Impressionist colleagues." (John Rewald, *The Paintings of Paul Cézanne, A Catalogue Raisonné*, New York, 1996, p. 194). They are as follows: *Portrait de Victor Chocquet*, 1876-77 (Rewald 292- Private collection); *Portrait de Victor Chocquet assis*, 1877 (Rewald 296- Columbus Gallery of Fine Arts, Ohio); *Portrait de Victor Chocquet (Buste)*, circa 1877 (Rewald 297- Virginia Museum of Fine Arts, Richmond); *Victor Chocquet d'après une photographie*; 1880-85 (Rewald 460-Louis Franck, Gstaad- Fondation Socindec); *Portrait de Victor Chocquet*, circa 1880 (Rewald 461- the present work); *Portrait de Victor Chocquet*, circa 1889 (Rewald 671- Private collection, Florence).

He made a final appearance in Cézanne's oeuvre in the sketch for the homage to the painter they both admired so much, *Apothéose de Delacroix*, 1890-1894 (Rewald 746). In the company of Cézanne himself, Pissarro and Monet, Chocquet kneels in admiration before the vision of Delacroix ascending into the clouds, a singular honor for the only non-painter in the group. The affection which Chocquet aroused is eaqually apparent in the two portraits that Renoir painted of him in the mid-1870s (Oskar Reinhart Collection, Am Römerholz, Winterthur and Fogg Art Museum, Harvard University Art Museum, Cambridge, Mass.)

Pierre-August Renoir (1841-1919)
Victor Chocquet, c. 1875
Oil on canvas *20 ⅞ by 17 ⅛ in.*
Courtesy of the Fogg Art Museum,
Harvard University Art Museums. Bequest of
Grenville L. Winthrop

Rewald speculates that the present work may have been painted from a drawing (Chappuis no. 394), possibly done from life, although the bust, collar and necktie correspond to the photograph used in Rewald 460. Small in scale, it is nonetheless a touching memento of Cézanne's admiration for his friend.

Provenance:
Ambroise Vollard, Paris (stockbook no. 3897 [A], acquired from the artist between 1899 and 1904)
Auguste Pellerin, Paris
Private collection

Exhibited:
Paris, Orangerie, *Hommage à Cézanne*, 1954, no. 46

Literature:
Georges Rivière, *Le Maitre Paul Cézanne*, 1923, p. 201
Wayne Andersen, "Cézanne, Tanguy, Chocquet,"*Art Bulletin* 49, no. 2, June 1967, illustrated fig. 6
John Rewald, *The Paintings of Paul Cézanne, A Catalogue Raisonné,* London and New York, 1996, vol. I, p. 311, no. 461; vol. II, no. 461, illustrated p. 148

107 Paul Cézanne (1839-1906)

PORTRAIT DE PAUL CEZANNE

Oil on canvas
18 ⅛ by 15 in.   46 by 38 cm.

Painted *circa* 1862-1864.

$600,000–800,000

Paul Cézanne, *Self-Portrait,* 1878-80
Oil on canvas, *23 ¾ by 18 ½ in.*
Acquired 1928. The Phillips Collection,
Washington, D.C.

Dated as early as 1858-1861 by Venturi (later revised to 1861), when the artist would have only been nineteen to twenty-one years of age, this brooding self-portrait has been more plausibly dated 1862-1864 by John Rewald. It is presumed to have been based on a photograph said to have been taken in 1861 although Cézanne modified it by cropping it at the level of his chest and substituting a black background for the pale tone of the photograph. In doing so he exaggerated its romantic potential by painting the jacket a murky reddish-brown and giving demonic highlights to his face. As Lawrence Gowing observed: "The intensity of gaze and the dour, grey modelling, flecked with accents of blood-red at emotionally crucial points, lead one to suspect a critical moment in the young man's fortunes, perhaps a crisis in the plans of the artist-to-be or the emergence of a private determination in the face of his father's opposition. He never, that we know of, painted in such a manner or under such pressure again." (Lawrence Gowing, *Cézanne The Early Years 1854-1872,* exhibition catalogue, London, 1988, p. 72).

At this stage in his career it seems that Cézanne could only contemplate his own image with the aid of a photograph. A decade or more later in the self-portraits in the Musée d'Orsay (Rewald 182), a private collection, Paris (Rewald 274) and the Phillips Collection, Washington, D.C. (Rewald 383), he subjected his own appearance to the most intense scrutiny, faithfully recording the changes that occurred as he aged and matured. Shortly after painting the present work, characterized by the smooth application of the medium, Cézanne began to explore the expressive potential of paint itself in the extensive series of works painted largely with the palette-knife. (See lot 108)

As the earliest surviving self-portrait, the present work is of particular significance, not only as a reflection of his state of mind at this critical juncture in his development but also as a benchmark against which the numerous later self-portraits can be measured. As in the early self-portraits of Picasso there is a strong component of self-dramatization in the demonic aspect he was able to extract from the relatively innocuous photographic source. This is the face of the artist whose inner conflicts can be seen so clearly expressesed in the troubled atmosphere of the early work. With greater maturity, emotional and artistic, the melodrama evaporated until in one of the last self-portraits, *Portrait de l'artiste au béret,* 1898-1900 (Rewald 834- Museum of Fine Arts, Boston), Cézanne achieved what John Rewald referred to as a "detachment which lends a nearly abstract aspect to the work, which assembles almost immaterial flat surfaces of perfect equipose." (Rewald 1996, no. 834, p. 499)

107

Provenance:
Paul Cézanne *fils*, Paris
Auguste Pellerin, Paris (by 1923)
Private collection

Exhibited:
Lyon, Musée de Lyon, *Centenaire de Paul Cézanne* 1939, no. 1
Paris, Bibliothèque Nationale, *Emile Zola*, 1952, no. 39
London, Royal Academy of Arts; Paris, Musée d'Orsay; Washington, D.C.,
National Gallery of Art, *Cézanne, The Early Years 1859-1872*, 1988-1989, no. 2

Literature:
Hans von Wedderkop, "Paul Cézanne," *Cicerone*, August 16, 1922, illustrated p. 683
Hans von Wedderkop, *Paul Cézanne*, Leipzig, 1922, illustrated
Georges Rivière, *Le Maître Paul Cézanne*, Paris, 1923, p. 196
John Rewald, *Cézanne and Zola*, Paris, 1936, illustrated fig. 4 (reprint, *Cézanne, sa vie, son oeuvre*, Paris, 1939, illustrated fig. 10; in English, *Paul Cézanne, A Biography*, New York, 1948, illustrated fig. 10)
Lionello Venturi, *Cézanne: Son Art- Son Oeuvre*, Paris, 1936, vol. I, p. 71, no. 18; vol. II, no. 18, illustrated pl. 5
Fritz Novotny, *Cézanne und das Ende der Wissenschaftlichen Perspektive*, Vienna, 1938, pp. 101-102, note 94
Germain Bazin, *L'Epoque impressioniste*, Paris, 1948, illustrated pl. 1
Bernard Dorival, *Cézanne*, Paris, 1948, illustrated pl. 1
Robert Ratcliffe, "Cézanne's Working Methods and Their Theoretical Background", (unpublished doctoral thesis, University of London, 1960)
Kurt Leonard, "Paul Cézanne", in *Selbstzeugnissen und Bilddokumenten*, Rheinbek bei Hamburg, 1966, illustrated p. 78
Phoebe Pool, *Impressionism*, New York, 1967, illustrated pl. 7
Meyer Schapiro, *Paul Cézanne*, Paris, 1973, illustrated p. 56
Frank Elgar, *Cézanne*, New York, 1975, illustrated pl. 6
Cézanne, exhibition catalogue, Grand Palais, Paris; Tate Gallery, London; Philadelphia Museum of Art, 1996, p. 146, illustrated
John Rewald, *The Paintings of Paul Cézanne, A Catalogue Raisonné*, London and New York, 1996, vol. I, p. 83, no. 72; vol. II, no. 72, illustrated p. 22

107 *(detail)*

108 Paul Cézanne (1839-1906)

L'ONCLE DOMINIQUE COIFFE D'UN
TURBAN

Oil on canvas
18 by 15 in.   45.5 by 38 cm.

Painted *circa* 1866.

$1,500,000–2,500,000

Among the most patient of Cézanne's models in the 1860's was Dominique
Aubert, a bailiff, the younger brother of Cézanne's mother. He has entered art
history as "L'Oncle Dominique", owing to the group of ten portraits that
Cézanne painted of him *circa*1866. In later years Cézanne was known for the
deliberations of his technique but in this period it was his impetuosity that
impressed his friends. Writing to Emile Zola in November 1866, Antony
Valabrégue said: ``Fortunately, I only posed for one day. The Uncle is more often
the model. Every afternoon, there appears a portrait of him while Guillemet
belabors it with terrible jokes."

Using the palette knife and far more generous supplies of paint than Courbet
ever used, Cézanne evolved the idiom that is frequently characterized as "couillarde"or "ballsy," derived from the French word for testicles (``couilles").
Lawrence Gowing gave a vivid description of this manner: "The extent of his
output in itself was astonishing and the assurance with which he accomplished it
was quite new in his works. The technical means became the basis for a unity of
pictorial ends. The consistency with which the paint was handled made it a
foundation stone, which its material character rather resembled. In this it was
analogous to the part that paint-handling was playing in the style of his contemporaries with whom he was to exhibit eight years later. In every other way
Cézanne's *couillarde* style was the antithesis of Impressionism. It was as unified
as Impressionism was fragmentary. At first the little palette-knife portraits were
on the edge of naïveté, but as they developed they became monumental."
(Lawrence Gowing, *Cézanne, The Early Years 1859-1872*, exhibition catalogue,
London, 1988, p. 104)

Henri Loyrette has also referred to the significance of the period 1865-1866 in
the development of Cézanne's career:
   "It was in 1865-66 that Cézanne became a painter. Hithero, it must be
   acknowledged, his art was limited to a few tentative efforts whose laudable
   intentions were thwarted by technical limitations. Zola was to gloss such a
   moment in his own evolution with an aphorism that sums up Cézanne's
   entire history: "One is born a poet, one becomes a worker." In the mid-
   1860s Cézanne the "poet", with only a few awkward canvases to his credit,
   set about turning himself into a worker. The Portrait played a crucial role in
   this reorientation. In Aix, where he spent the late summer and fall of 1866,
   Cézanne painted many portraits of those close to him, using a variety of for-
   mats; the resulting works include the full-length depiction of his father reading *L'Èvenement*, the rough oil sketch *Marion and Valabrègue Setting Out for
   the Motif*, and an impressive series of portraits of his maternal uncle, the
   bailiff Dominique Aubert.

108

Paul Cézanne, *Portrait of Uncle Dominique,*
c. 1865-67. Oil on canvas, *18 by 15 in.*
Norton Simon Art Foundation, Pasadena, CA

Ten canvases from this sustained and productive painting campaign survive, picturing Uncle Dominique in full face, profile, and three-quarter views, in bust and half length, behatted, beturbaned, and becapped. All were executed with a palette knife- also Courbet's favorite painting implement at this time- in the broad, impassioned *couillarde* style, and in emphatically contrasted blacks and whites reminiscent of Manet. These are indeed the two artists who must be invoked in connection with this remarkable series, but Cézanne was already outstripping their transgressive lessons. Guillemet sensed this when, in a letter to his friend the Puerto Rican painter Francisco Oller, he praised the revolutionary power of these new works: "Courbet becomes a classic. He's done some superb things, next to Manet he's traditional, and Manet will one day seem so in turn next to Cézanne...Today's gods will not be tomorrow's, to arms, let our febrile hands seize hold of the knife of insurrection, let's tear down and rebuild...Paint with heavy impasto and dance on the belly of the terrified bourgeois."

Cézanne approached the portrait in the same spirit that he did the landscape, focusing as closely on facial asperities as on geographical idiosyncracies, on the particulars of individual features as on the geological strata in the environs of Aix and the Gulf of Marseille. But, just as he did not hesitate to add an elaborate factory complex to an otherwise accurately described site, so, too, did he provide the patient and compliant bailiff with imaginary lives: Dominique Aubert was cast in turn as a cowled monk with a cross around his neck, an artisan in a worker's smock, or a lawyer in toque and collar. The larger meaning of these masquerades remains a subject of conjecture: perhaps Cézanne was making a visual pun when he transformed Dominique into a Dominican (he resorted to a similar play of words and image in his portrait of Achille Emperaire), perhaps the lawyer costume was meant to evoke one of his first defenders, perhaps the artisan's smock signaled the new orientation of his art. In any case, Uncle Dominque is a figure comparable to Manet's Victorine Meurent and Degas's Emma Dobigny: models whose pronounced individuality renders them recognizable from one painting to the next despite their many disguises. And these costumes- whether flimsy (the worker's smock sits haphazardly on top of the bailiff's own dark suit) or deliberately inaccurate (the toque and the collar are the same blue-gray color)- are but pretexts for successive metamorphoses: the bailiff, his arms crossed, meditates, or, flattened against a crude white expanse like an icon against its gold ground, blesses rather than pleads with the authority of a Christ Pantocrator." (Henri Loyrette in *Cézanne,* exhibition catalogue, Paris and Phildelphia, 1996, pp. 88-89).

Paul Cézanne, *Dominique Aubert, the Artist's Uncle, as a monk,* c. 1866
The Metropolitan Museum of Art,The Walter H. and Leonore Annenberg Collection,Partial Gift of Walter H. and Leonore Annenberg, 1933 (1933.400.1) Photograph ©1994 The Metropolitan Museum of Art

Remarkably Auguste Pellerin owned seven of the ten portraits of Uncle Dominique- Norton Simon Art Foundation, Pasadena (Rewald 102); Private collection (Rewald 103); Private collection (Rewald 104); the present work (Rewald 105); Musée d'Orsay (Rewald 106); Metropolitan Museum of Art (Rewald 107); Private collection, New York (Rewald 109).

Auguste Pellerin, as mentioned elsewhere (see introduction pp. 10-13) was as great a collector of Manet as was of Cézanne before the latter superseded him in his esteem. It is a fascinating reflection of the coherence of Pellerin's taste that these uncompromising portraits by Cézanne, indebted to Manet but disavowing his influence at the same time, should have had such a strong appeal to him.

This work is recorded in the Vollard Archives, photo. no. 345 (annotated by Cézanne's son: *Aubert 1865*)

Provenance:
Ambroise Vollard, Paris (stockbook no. 3890 [A], acquired from the artist between 1899 and 1904 for 75 francs)
Auguste Pellerin, Paris
Private collection

Exhibited:
Paris, Orangerie, *Hommage à Paul Cézanne*, 1954, no. 7
London, Royal Academy of Arts; Paris, Musée d'Orsay; Washington D.C., National Gallery of Art, *Cézanne, The Early Years 1859-1872*, 1988-1989, no. 20

Literature:
Georges Rivière, *Le Maître Paul Cézanne*, Paris, 1923, p. 202
Lionello Venturi, *Cézanne: Son Art, Son Oeuvre*, Paris, 1936, vol. 1, p. 84, no. 82; vol. II, no. 82, illustrated pl. 21
Douglas Cooper, "Cézanne's Chronology", *Burlington Magazine 98*, December 1956, p. 449
John Rewald, *The Paintings of Paul Cézanne, A Catalogue Raisonné*, London and New York, 1996, vol. I, p. 101, no. 105; vol. II, no. 105, illustrated p. 34

109 Paul Cézanne (1839-1906)

CINQ BAIGNEUSES SOUS DES
ARBRES

Oil on canvas
23 ⅜ by 28 ¾ in. 60 by 73 cm.

Painted *circa* 1875.

$6,000,000–8,000,000

Paul Cézanne, *Baigneurs au Repos*
Oil on canvas, *35 by 45.5 cm*
Photo: Maurice Aeschimann
© Musée d'art et d'histoire, (Fondation Jean-
Louis Prevost), Geneva, Inv. no 1985-17

For over forty years Cézanne pondered the theme of naked bathers in a land-scape setting, a subject that was eventually to culminate in three of his greatest masterpieces, the three paintings of bathers in the National Gallery, London, the Barnes Foundation, Merion, Pa. and the Philadelphia Museum of Art (Rewald, 855-857). Although a number of his early works depict figures clad in modern dress in the the open air (see lot 114), from the mid-1870s onwards Cézanne focused on the nude figure in landscape surroundings. Clearly this was a theme that found its origins in the art of the museums rather than in any aspects of contemporary life since even such bathing as there was always was done fully-clad. In the interpretation of the early paintings of bathers, a group to which the work under discussion belongs, the extent of Cézanne's indebtedness to particular sources in the old masters and to the exploration of themes sanctified by them is still a matter of controversy.

John Rewald associates *Cinq baigneuses sous des arbres* with the earliest group of works devoted to this theme, studies of isolated bathers (Rewald nos. 248, 249, 252, 253, 255, 262, and 263) as well as groups of nudes (Rewald nos. 250, 251, 254, 256, 258, 259-61). He sees the origins of the endeavor in "the work in the open to which he applied himself at Pontoise and Auvers-sur-Oise" and refers to a letter addressed to Zola in the fall of 1866 in which he said: "You see, all pictures done inside, in the studio, will never be as good as those executed in the open. When representing plein-air scenes, the contrast between the figures and the ground are astonishing, and the landscape is magnificent. I perceive superb things and I must resolve to work out-of-doors." (Quoted Rewald, 1996, p. 172) It was not until the mid-1870s when the example of Pissarro rapidly led to the almost total suppression of imaginary subjects in favor of a method of working based on observation of the natural world that Cézanne embarked on his first group of bather compositions. Rewald continues his discussion of the present painting by acknowledging the relevance of old-master sources but rejecting most specific references: "But the difficulty of having professional models pose outside- not to speak of the cost- apparently led the artist to make use of his academic studies (though only a very few of them still exist) in addition to his recollections from museums. Berthold cites an engraving by Marcantonio Raimondi, a naiad by Rubens, and a painting by Delacroix among the sources for some of the bathers of his compositions. These connections are extremely interesting so long as one remembers that Cézanne did not copy such sources, but that, thanks to his enormous visual appetite, he absorbed countless images, which he subsequently recalled when he needed them." (ibid p. 177)

Other commentators have instead emphasized the relationship between the early bathers and the fantasy scenes that immediately preceded them. Noteworthy in this respect is the extended commentary given by Mary Louise Krumrine in her catalogue of the exhibition *Paul Cézanne Die Badenden* held at the Kunstmuseum Basel in 1989. After tracing back Cézanne's absorption in the theme to a sketch on the back of a letter to Zola dated June 20, 1859, she proceeds to analyze the relationships between *La Baignade*, 1875-1877 (Rewald 251- private collection, Japan) and the work under discussion. She likens the provocative gesture of the figure on the left to the temptress in *La Tentation de Saint Antoine, circa*1877 (Rewald 300-Musée d'Orsay) and refers to the "serpentine shape" of the branch which the central figure is trying to reach (Krumrine, pp. 107, 115).

"A counterpart to these *Baigneurs* may be the contemporary *Cinq Baigneuses*, where the three central nudes are posed in the same manner as the three males in *La Baignade*. The tree no longer divides the canvas but grows from the river bank at the left. Its trunk and branches bend over and toward the bathers, but the mood has changed, along with the sex of the bathers: the provocatively posed figure stepping into the water is seen from the back in a swaying contraposto that

111 Paul Cézanne (1839-1906)

LA LUTTE D'AMOUR

Oil on canvas
17 ¼ by 22 ⅛ in.   44 by 56.5 cm.

Painted *circa* 1879-1880.

$4,000,000–6,000,000

This painting and the second version - *La Lutte d'Amour*, II, *circa* 1880 (Rewald 456- The National Gallery of Art, Washington, D.C.)- have generated widely different interpretations in recent years. For Meyer Schapiro suggestions of violence far outweighed any more benign characteristics; he described the subject as "a theme out of Venetian art, perhaps by way of a Poussinist artist, but... conceived in another mood. The Renaissance bacchanals are scenes that combine love-play, drinking, and dancing; they are images of gayety and joyous release. Cézanne's painting is of a stuggle, the violence of love, even rape. Four men attack four women; a leaping dog adds another note of animality. These are not pagan idyllic nudes from Greek mythology, but a modern fantasy like Cézanne's solemn picnic of clothed and nude figures. The multiplication of figures increases the violence, but also makes it more natural, an action of men and not a solitary crime."(Meyer Schapiro, *Paul Cézanne*, New York, 1962, p. 48).

Kurt Badt, who refered to *La Lutte d'Amour* as a "strange and magnificent composition," saw a symbolic significance in the choreography of the works, ``established by the presence in a conspicuous spot, of a dog; according to Cézanne's own exploration of his *Apotheosis of Delacroix*, he saw in this animal the embodiment of envy and jealousy."(Kurt Badt, Munich, 1956, p. 85). More recently Mary Louise Krumrine has referred to the pair of paintings as "probably Cézanne's last scenes of overt sexual aggression... In *La Lutte d'Amour* we have four pairs of figures in varying postures and with varying degrees of bodily contact. The awkward and indistinct forms are probably drawn from Cézanne's own imagination... The underlying harshness of this *Lutte d'amour* contrast with the pleasing blues and greens of the landscape and the billowing clouds, that repeat the shapes and movements of the figures. They seem weighed down by the dark strokes that outline them and the objects in the landscape. Equally somber, even frightening, is the leaping black dog who is balanced by the black pattern on which a nude reclines in the opposite corner. And it is tempting to see the voyeur as a version of the ruddy and rubicund Priapus, poised on his toes and wantonly gazing at the sleeping nymph under the trees." (Mary Louise Krumrine, pp. 58, 63).

While acknowledging the provocative nature of many of these interpretations, John Rewald preferred to be less dogmatic in his masterful summary of various commentaries: "We do know that the young author of such dramatic and pathos-filled compositions as *L'Enlèvement, L'Autopsie, Le Meurtre, La Femme étranglée,* and *Tentation de Saint Antoine* had a superb ability to combine mood and movement- even agitation- with powerful contrasts of color. Some of this emotional urgency also appeared in his early portraits, still lifes, and landscapes. On the other hand, we know that, by contrast, the aging artist mostly envisioned groups of naked women in Arcadian settings and that the portraits, still lifes, and landscapes of his later years seem stripped of emotional emphasis. Who is to say that the wishful dreams of the middle-aged Cézanne- halfway between the work of his beginnings and that of his last phase- were still dominated by passion and violence?"

Paul Cézanne, *The Battle of Love*, c. 1880
Gift of the W. Averell Harriman Foundation in memory of Marie N. Harriman. © 1997 Board of Trustees, National Gallery of Art, Washington

111

38

The attitudes of the couples he painted here are, to put it mildly, ambiguous. The grotesque clasp of the two nudes tumbling down the hillside at right could mean strangulation as well as innocent love-play. Do the women fight the men or do they simply provoke and entice them? Might Cézanne not have thought here of an idyll with lovers frolicking against a beautiful background? And if the black animal is, indeed, a Freudian equivalent for various instincts, it may also be a memory of a dog named Black, who escorted the painter and his friends on their boyhood excursions around Aix, a faithful companion rather than a symbol of evil.

Finally, there are the bright colors, so alien to any conscious dramatic intent. The sunny atmosphere actually adds a touch of exuberance to the scene (more so in the second version than in this one). The only contrast is provided by the dark, standing figure at left, which detaches itself powerfully against the deep blue sea and the luminous sky. This man seems to plead with the woman at his feet rather than to threaten her. His counterpart is the dog, adding a dark accent to the right corner of the composition." (John Rewald, *The Paintings of Paul Cézanne, A Catalogue Raisonné*, 1996, pp. 306-307)

Titian (*circa* 1490-1576), *The Bacchanal*, c. 1520 © Museo del Prado, Madrid, All rights reserved

Although the meaning of the composition is the subject of debate, there is general agreement on the old-master antecedents. Titian's *Bacchanal* in the Prado, *The Andrians* in the Louvre as well as his *Bacchus and Ariadne* in the National Gallery, London have all been mentioned in the pedigree (see Rewald, 1996, p. 307). John Rewald believed that Ruben's Mythological subjects were of the same family while Meyer Schapiro saw hints of Delacroix in *Jacob Wrestling with the Angel* in the chapel of Saint-Sulpice, Paris in the raised arms of the couple near the black dog. In both versions of the painting and in the related watercolor (John Rewald, *Paul Cézanne, The Watercolors*, Boston, 1983, no. 60) the disposition of the figures is virtually identical but stylistically there are major differences. The present picture, the earlier of the two, is much more deliberate in execution and darker in tonality. Cézanne has used his diagonal, "constructive" stroke to impose a discipline on the strenuous activities of the four couples. In The National Gallery version, the touch is lighter and more spontaneous. The horizon line has been lowered, creating more space for the billowing clouds that echo the rhythms of the figures. Grounded in the first version, the elevated couple on the hillock or far right is about to the fall into the lake in the second. Before entering the Pellerin collection, the canvas under discussion had belonged to Camille Pissaro while Renoir owned the second version. Both artists must have found the enigmatic paintings full of suggestions for their own figure compositions.

This work is recorded in the Vollard Archives, photo. no. 399 (annotated by Cézanne's son: *1878*)

Provenance:
Camille Pissarro, Paris
Bernheim-Jeune, Paris
Auguste Pellerin, Paris
Private collection

Exhibited:
Paris, Orangerie, *Cézanne*, 1936, no. 66
Paris, Orangerie, *Hommage à Cézanne*, 1954, no. 37
Basel, Kunstmuseum, *Paul Cézanne: die Badenden,* 1989, no. 40
Paris, Grand Palais, *Paul Cézanne: Une Retrospective*; London, Tate Gallery; Philadelphia Museum of Art, *Cézanne*, 1995-1996, no. 64

Literature:
Maurice Denis, "Cézanne" , *Burlington Magazine*16, no. 82, Jan. 1910, illustrated p. 247

Maurice Denis, "Cézanne," *Kunstbladet*, 1909-1910, illustrated p. 247

J. Thiis, *Kunst og Kultur*, 1912, illustrated p. 19

Fritz Burger, *Cézanne und Hodler*, Munich, 1913, illustrated pl. 52 (5th edition, Munich, 1923, illustrated pl. 55)

Fritz Burger, *Einführung in die moderne Kunst*, Berlin, 1917, illustrated fig. 129

Maestri Moderni, Rome, 1920, illustrated

"Courier de la presse," *Bulletin de la Vie Artistique*, 1921, illustrated p. 51

Joachim Gasquet, *Cézanne*, Paris, 1921, illustrated opp. p. 48

Atzouji Zeisho, *Paul Cézanne*, Tokyo, 1921, illustrated fig. 33

Julius Meir-Graefe, *Cézanne und sein Kreis*, Munich, 1922, illustrated p. 193

Curt Glaser, *Paul Cézanne*, Leipzig, 1922, illustrated pl. 10

Georges Rivière, *Le Maitre Paul Cézanne*, Paris, 1923, p. 205

Joachim Gasquet, *Cézanne*, Paris, 1926, illustrated

Curt Glaser, "Das Cézanne- Buch Joachim Gasquets, I, " *Kunst und Künstler* 25, 1927, illustrated p. 329

Eugenio d'Ors, *Paul Cézanne*, Paris, 1930, illustrated pl. 38 (In English: New York, 1936, illustrated pl. 53)

Beaux Arts, May 22, 1936, illustrated p. 10

Maurice Raynal, *Cézanne*, Paris, 1936, illustrated pl. XCIX

Gilles de la Tourette, "Paul Cézanne," *Art et les Artists*, July 1936, illustrated p. 331

Lionello Venturi, *Cézanne: Son Art, Son Oeuvre*, Paris, 1936, vol. I, p. 147, no. 379; vol. II, no. 379, illustrated pl. 104

G. di San Lazzaro, *Paul Cézanne*, Paris, 1938, illustrated fig. 53

Albert C. Barnes and Violette de Mazia, *The Art of Cézanne*, New York, 1939, no. 49, illustrated p. 182

Bernard Dorival, *Cézanne*, Paris, 1948, p. 48, illustrated pl. IV

Gotthard Jedlicka, *Cézanne*, Berne, 1948, illustrated fig. 16

Liliane Guerry, *Cézanne et l'expression de l'espace*, Paris, 1950, pp. 56-58

Francis Jourdain, *Cézanne*, Paris and New York, 1950, illustrated

Douglas Cooper, "Two Cézanne Exhibitions,"*Burlington Magazine* 96, no. 620, Nov. 1954, pp. 348-349

Maurice Raynal, *Cézanne*, Geneva, 1954, illustrated p. 19

Lawrence Gowing, "Notes on the Development of Cézanne," *Burlington Magazine* 98, no. 639, June 1956, pp. 185-192

Douglas Cooper, "Cézanne's Chronology" , *Burlington Magazine* 98, December 1956, p. 449

Kurt Badt, *Die Kunst Cézannes*, Munich, 1956, p. 85 (In English: *The Art of Cézanne*, Berkeley and Los Angeles, 1965, p. 112)

Meyer Schapiro, "The Apples of Cézanne: An Essay on the meaning of still life,"*Art News Annual* 34, 1968, p. 39

Meyer Schapiro, *Paul Cézanne*, Paris, 1973, illustrated pl. 8

Bernard Dorival, "Les Omissions d'Archipenko et de Lipschitz," *Bulletin de la Société de l'Histoire de L'Art Français*, 1974, illustrated fig. 65

Lionello Venturi, *Cézanne*, Geneva, 1978, illustrated p. 124

G. Ballasin, *Norms and Variations in Art, Essays in Honor of Moshe Barasch*, Jerusalem, 1983, p. 185

Denis Coutagne, *Cézanne au Musée d'Aix*, exhibition catalogue, Aix en Provence, 1984, illustrated p. 190

Ronald Pickvance, *Cézanne*, exhibition catalogue, Tokyo, Kobe and Nagoya, 1986, illustrated p. 86

John Rewald, *The Paintings of Paul Cézanne, A Catalogue Raisonné,* London and New York, 1996, vol. I pp. 306-307, no. 455; vol. II, no. 455, illustrated p. 146

112 Paul Cézanne (1839-1906)

UNE MODERNE OLYMPIA (OR LE PACHA)

Oil on canvas
22 ¼ by 21 ⅝ in.   56.5 by 55 cm.

Painted *circa* 1870.

$6,000,000–8,000,000

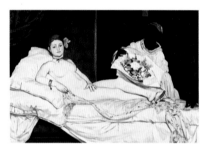

Edouard Manet (1832-1883), *Olympia*, 1863.
Musée d'Orsay, Paris
© Photo RMN-H. Lewandowski

Paul Cézanne, *Tentation de Saint Antoine*,
c. 1875. Musée d'Orsay, Paris.
© Photo RMN-Hervé Lewandowski

Cézanne painted two versions of *Une Moderne Olympia*- the present picture, also known as *Le Pacha* and the canvas in the Musée d'Orsay, painted 1873-1874 and exhibited at the First Impressionist Exhibition of 1874. Both represent a naked courtesan and an attendant being observed by a clothed male figure seen from behind but differ considerably in style, the earlier of the two extravagantly baroque in feeling, the later far more rococo in its deftness. Cézanne withdrew to L'Estaque after the outbreak of the Franco-Prussian War on July 18, 1870 and it was probably there that he painted the series of visionary works to which the first version belongs. Lawrence Gowing (v. i. p. 161) referred to a "Flaubertian vein of fantastic sensuality", that runs through the whole group, including *Pastorale*(Rewald 166), *La Tentation de Saint-Antoine* (Rewald 167) and *Le Déjeuner sur l'herbe* (Rewald 164).

Manet's *Dejeuner sur l'herbe* had been shown at the Salon des Refusés in 1863. Two years later *Olympia* was shown at the Salon where it greatly affected Cézanne, staying in his mind until 1870 when he decided to "update" it, to pro-duce a "modern"version. As Götz Adriani has observed : "Cézanne worked on the assumption that he could only achieve a comparable *succès de scandale* by developing Manet's technical and iconographical innovations even more uncom-promisingly, creating examples of even more bold sensuality with which to con-front the public. And what better to build on than *Olympia*, the Salon outrage, which upset the public and the press as no painting had done before." (Götz Adriani, "'La lutte d'amour,' notes on Cézanne's early figure scenes" in *Cézanne The Early Years 1854-1872*, exhibition catalogue, London, 1988, p. 45).

For the pose of the reclining courtesan Manet had looked back to the nudes of Titian and Goya, treating them with respect but with considerable irony. Cézanne's references to Manet were to be far less respectful. In the watercolors, *Le Punch au rhum*, 1866-1867 and *L'Aprés -midi à Naples*, 1870-1872 (John Rewald, *Paul Cézanne, The Watercolors,* Boston, 1983, nos. 34 and 35), for exam-ple, which have been seen as commentaries on *Olympia*, the cool elegance of Manet is replaced by a deliberately outrageous assault on bourgeois *mores* and insistence on academic perfection. In the slightly later watercolor in the Philadelphia Museum of Art, *Olympia* (Rewald, ibid. no. 135) the pose of the nude is analogous to Manet's courtesan but the dynamics of the original compo-sition have been transferred by the inclusion of the male visitor *behind* the bed on which she lies. In the two canvases under discussion, however, the semi-recumbent nude is closer to his own early *La Madeleine pénitente* than to Manet, as Mary Louise Krumrine observed. (Mary Louise Krumrine, *Paul Cézanne, The Bathers*, Kunstmuseum, Basel, 1989, p. 83). The cool elegance of Manet's reclin-ing figure has been replaced by the hunched over position of Cézanne's nude, crouching on her bed. Similar serpentine rhythms unite the courtesan, her atten-dant, the observer and the gargantuan decorative elements, the red curtain held back by golden cords, the vase of flowers towering over the seated nude and the billows of the bed clothes that swoop down to the left foreground. Even the titan-supported table with its display of overripe fruit is massive in scale.

Discussing the nature of the relationship between Cézanne's "modern" version and Manet's masterpiece, Lawrence Gowing eloquently conveyed the idiosyn-cratic nature of Cézanne's achievement: "Like his *Déjeuner sur l'Herbe* of around 1870, Cézanne's *Modern Olympia* has an evident relationship to Manet's noted masterpiece which originated the title. Yet the precise reference is not readily defined. Roger Fry observed that it was not easy to specify any but an ironic meaning in Cézanne's *Modern Olympia*, but the vision 'clumsy and almost ridiculous as it is, imposes itself on us by its indubitable accent of sincerety.' In fact, the content of these pictures has been the subject of considerable doubt. It should be observed that all these variatons contain an element which is lacking

Paul Cézanne, *Une Moderne Olympia*, c. 1873-1874. Musée d'Orsay, Paris. © Photo RMN-Hervé Lewandowski

in the famous themes that they follow. They all contain, usually in the foreground, a figure that is identifiable as their painter, Cézanne himself. No figure that could be associated with Manet ever appeared in the canvases that initiated these themes. On the contrary, Manet was conspicuously absent and was perhaps open to criticism for that fact. Cézanne had no admiration for impersonality in painting. He and Zola felt rather the signs of temperament that identified a painter were the essence of his contribution. Similarly, the reticence of Manet's *taches* and the neutrality of the atmosphere in which his subjects materialized were quite unlike the bulging volumes curvaceously outlined in Cézanne's modernisation of *Olympia*, and from the stormy evening light established with originality and beauty in the similarly modernized *Déjeuner sur l'Herbe*. The fact that Cézanne's versions of *Olympia* have always been described as 'modern', certainly by his wish, is significant. It implies that reticent tone painting seemed to Zola and Cézanne to be in the circumstances of the 1860s archaic, and the impersonality with which Manet was felt to emit the tone, not using it to expressive purpose, but merely spitting it out, was certainly regarded as a criticism- a criticism that Cézanne's farouche compositions of 1870 implicitly launched and intentionally escaped. Manet was lacking in temperament and the fact pointed to a shortcoming in the endeavour to re-establish tone painting, painting in flat patches within defined contours on the model of the seventeenth century and particularly on the reticent pattern of Spanish painting.

The design of *Modern Olympia* has in fact an astonishing boldness, embellished with grandiose grotesqueries, exactly the qualities that the historicist *belle peinture* of the nineteenth century avoided and Fry was not the only critic that it left at a loss. From the standpoint of Cézanne's Impressionist contemporaries, inventive boldness was a serious obstacle to appreciation and it was avoided by the more scattered notation of Cézanne's second version of the subject painted at Auvers with the advice of Dr. Gachet in 1873 (Musée d'Orsay, Paris)." (Lawrence Gowing, in *Cézanne, The Early Years 1859-1872*, catalogue of the exhibition, London, Royal Academy of Arts; Paris, Musée d'Orsay; Washington, D.C., National Gallery of Art, 1988-1989, no. 40).

Cézanne's relationship to Manet, and through Manet, to the old masters was clearly highly complicated, compounded equally of respect for past achievements and rejection of the contemporary relevance of their solutions to pictorial problems. In attempting to `outdo' Manet, Cézanne offered an ironic commentary on his sources, extravagant in its idiosyncratic mannerisms, that still astonishes by its strangeness and modernity.

Provenance:
Estate of Paul Cézanne
Ambroise Vollard, Paris, and Bernheim-Jeune, Paris (acquired from the estate in February 1907)
Bernheim-Jeune, Paris
Auguste Pellerin, Paris (acquired from the above on November 14, 1908 in exchange for a Renoir *Fleurs*and cash)
Private collection

Exhibited:
Paris, Orangerie, *Cézanne*, 1936, no. 16
Paris, Orangerie, *Hommage à Cézanne*, 1954 no.19
London, Royal Academy of Arts; Paris, Musée d'Orsay; Washington, D.C.,
National Gallery of Art, *Cézanne, The Early Years 1859-1872*, 1988-1989, no. 40
Basel, Kunstmuseum, *Paul Cézanne:Die Badenden*, 1989, no. 4
Paris, Grand Palais, *Impressionisme, les Origines 1859-1869*; New York, The
Metropolitan Museum of Art, *Origins of Impressionism*, 1994-1996, no. 27
Paris, Grand Palais; London, Tate Gallery, Philadelphia Museum of Art, *Cézanne*,
1996, no. 27

Literature:
Julius Meier-Graefe, *Cézanne und sein Kreis*, Munich, 1918, illustrated p. 96
(Various editions: Munich, 1920, illustrated p. 96; Munich, 1922, illustrated p.
109)
Gustave Coquiot, *Paul Cézanne*, Paris, 1919, illustrated opp. p. 144
Curt Glaser, *Paul Cézanne*, Leipzig, 1922, illustrated pl. 4
Georges Rivière, *Le Maitre Paul Cézanne*, Paris, 1923, p. 202, illustrated opp. p. 50
Roger Fry, "Le développement de Cézanne,"*Amour de l'Art,* Dec. 1926, illustrated p. 391 (In English: *Cézanne: A study of his Development*, New York, 1927, illustrated pl. III, pp. 16-17)
Julius Meier-Graefe, *Cézanne*, London, 1927, illustrated pl. XI
Alan Burroughs, "David and Cézanne, presenting the case of Thought versus Feeling," *Arts* 16, no. 1, Sept. 1929, illustrated p. 111
Roger Fry, "Cézanne's Udvikling" , *Samleren*, 1929, illustrated p. 103
Eugenio d'Ors, *Paul Cézanne*, Paris, 1930, illustrated pl. 33 (In English: New York, 1936, illustrated pl. 46)
Georges Rivière, *Cézanne, Le Peintre solitaire,* Paris, 1933, illustrated p. 53 (New edition: Paris, 1942, illustrated p. 53)
Nina Iavorskia, *Cézanne*, Moscow, 1935, illustrated pl. 11
Maurice Raynal, *Cézanne*, Paris, 1936, illustrated pl. XVI
Lionello Venturi, *Cézanne: Son Art, son Oeuvre*, Paris, 1936, vol. 1, p. 90, no. 106; vol. II, no. 106, illustrated pl. 27
G. di San Lazzaro, *Paul Cézanne*, Paris, 1938, illustrated fig. 46
Albert C. Barnes and Violette de Mazia, *The Art of Cézanne*, New York, 1939, no. 33, illustrated p. 178
Goran Schildt, *Cézanne*, Stockholm, 1946, illustrated fig. 16
Bernard Dorival, *Cézanne*, Paris, 1948, illustrated pl. VIII
Liliane Guerry, *Cézanne et l'expression de l'espace,* Paris, 1950, illustrated fig. 3 (Reprint: Paris, 1966, illustrated pl. 1)
M. Florisoone, "Van Gogh et les peintres d'Auvers chez le Dr. Gachet," *Amour de l'Art*, 1952, illustrated p. 20
Kurt Badt, *Die Kunst Cézannes*, Munich, 1956, p. 76
S. Lovgren, *The Genesis of Modernism*, Stockholm, 1959, illustrated p. 33
Sara Lichtenstein, "Cézanne and Delacroix,"*Art Bulletin*, 46, no. 1, Mar. 1964, illustrated fig. 9
Meyer Schapiro, *Paul Cézanne*, Paris, 1973, illustrated p. 56
Lionello Venturi, *Cézanne*, Geneva, 1978, illustrated p. 56
Mary Louise Krumrine, "Cézanne's Bathers: Form and Content," *Arts* 54, no. 9, May 1980, p. 115
Mary Thompkins Lewis, *Cézanne's Early Imagery*, Berkeley, 1989, p. 201, illustrated fig. 107
John Rewald, *The Paintings of Paul Cézanne, A Catalogue Raisonné*, London and New York, 1996, vol. I, p. 137, no. 171; vol. II, no. 171, illustrated p. 59

113 Paul Cézanne (1839-1906)

LA TOILETTE FUNERAIRE (OR L'AU-
TOPSIE)

Oil on canvas
19½ by 31⅝ in.   49.5 by 80.5 cm.

Painted in 1869.

$700,000–900,000

Painted at a moment in Cézanne's career when imagery of violence prevailed in works such as *L'Enlèvement*, 1867 (Rewald 14) and *Le Meurtre, circa* 1870 (Rewald 165), the canvas variously known as *La toilette funéraire* or *L'Autopsie* represents a moment after the terminal violence has occurred. Whereas the rape and murder were expressed in compositions of baroque extravagance, the rigid body and its attendant figures in the present work evoke other types of seventeenth century art. Mary Thompkins Lewis has recently delineated the parallel strains of romanticism and realism in Cézanne's work of the 1860s and has shown how, like many of his realist contemporaries, he also gravitated to scenes of death (Mary Thompkins Lewis, *Cézanne's Early Imagery*, Berkely, Los Angeles, London, 1989, p. 121).   Known also as *L'Autopsie*, the present painting can be linked with paintings such as François Feyer-Perrin's *Une Leçon d'anatomie de Dr. Velpeau*, exhibited at the Salon of 1864, parodied by Daumier in *Le Charivari*, August 21, 1869. Thompkins continues: "While Roger Fry popularized the identification of this painting as an autopsy scene, many other scholars of Cézanne's oeuvre have referred to the painting as *La Toilette funéraire*, and a study of its imagery and sources reveals this to be the painting's true subject." Perhaps the extreme bleakness of Cézanne's canvas led to the misunderstanding of its subject. It is also true that burial preparation scenes were uncommon in nineteenth-century art; Courbet's analogous *La Toilette de la morte* suffered a similar fate and was mistitled for over half a century. Nonetheless, aside from its grim atmosphere and the undeniable presence of a cadavre, there is little in Cézanne's painting to suggest that it depicts an autopsy. There is the distinct omission of any scientific apparatus or the requisite scalpel; Cézanne shows only a small bowl of water, the corpse, and two attendant figures. The morbid atmosphere of the scene, which Fry called macabre, becomes more comprehensible in light of historical depictions of the dead Christ, a common source for this motif. Despite the declining interest in traditional religious subjects, this specific one continued to fascinate painters throughout the nineteenth century and was particularly important to Cézanne in the mid-1860s, just when he was experimenting with genre."(Lewis, ibid, p. 122)

The uncompromising harshness of the present work, the intense chiaroscuro of which only seems to emphasize the highlighted areas of strong color, owes much to Spanish art of the seventeenth century. Barnes and de Mazia noted the relationship between this work and a *Mise au tombeau* attributed to Ribera (acquired by the Louvre in 1858). Robert Ratcliffe pointed out the similarities between the heads of the attendant figures in the present composition with those in Ribera's *Christ au tombeau*, acquired in Spain in 1868 and first exhibited at the Louvre from the beginning of January 1869. A further parallel between the head of the bearded figure bending over the bed and a series of bald heads in Caravaggio's *Mort de la Vierge* in the Louvre was noted by Lawrence Gowing (Lawrence Gowing, *Cézanne The Early Years 1859-1872*, exhibition catalogue, London, 1988, p. 13). Cézanne's studies for the pose of the recumbent figure include not only drawings after Fra Bartholommeo della Porta's *Christ au tombeau*(Öffentliche Kunstsammlung, Kupferstichkabinett, Basel) but also drawings done from the model, probably at the Académie Suisse (Art Institute of Chicago).

Jusepe de Ribera, *dit* L'Espagnolet (1591-1652), *La Déposition du Christ,* Musée du Louvre, Paris. © Photo RMN-G. Blot/J. Schormans

113

Paul Cézanne, Study for "L'Autopsie",
charcoal, with stumping, on tan laid paper,
c.1867-69, *32 by 48.7 cm*
Gift of Tiffany and Margaret Blake, 1947.36
Photograph ©1997 The Art Institute of
Chicago. All Rights Reserved.

Growing out of Cézanne's enthusiasm for the tenebrism of painters such as Ribera and Caravaggio, *La Toilette Funéraire* or *L'Autopsie* may be as deeply rooted in his turbulent inner life as other works of the period. Mary Louise Krumrine (v.i, 45) suggests that there may be a parallel between the three figures in Cézanne's painting and the characters in Zola's *Thérèse Raquin*, the lovers Laurent and Thérèse who plot to murder Thérèse's husband, Camille. Zola drew heavily on Cézanne for the character of Laurent, and described Laurent haunting the morgue every day as he searches for the corpse of Camille. Certainly the bald and bearded figure in the painting bears a strong physical resemblance to Cézanne. For Lewis, however, the literary parallels are far less significant than the obvious references to a wide range of sources in the old masters and cultural trends of the 1860s. She describes Cézanne's *La Toilette Funéraire* as "both a tribute to these earlier masters of realism (Caravaggio and Ribera) and a secularized mise-au-tombeau. The radically secular tone of Renan's popular *La Vie de Jésus* (1863) encouraged experiments of this type; some of the most successful death images of the decade were paintings that combined traditionally several motifs with aspects of the mundane...Few nineteenth century painters, however, were as successful as Cézanne was in capturing the raw intensity of baroque death imagery. In *La Toilette Funéraire* he preserved the emotive power of the era by using its own models and devices and in so doing produced an image whose spirit and sense of realism belong to the past." (Mary Thompkins Lewis, ibid., p. 129).

This work is recorded in the Vollard Archives, photo. no. 98 (annotated by Cézanne's son: *1865*)

Provenance:
Ambroise Vollard, Paris (stockbook no. 3306 [A], acquired from the artist between 1899 and 1904)
Auguste Pellerin, Paris
Private collection

Exhibited:
Paris, Orangerie, *Monticelli et le baroque provençal*, 1953, no. 7
Paris, Orangerie, *Hommage à Cézanne*, 1954, no. 14
Basel, Galerie Beyeler, *Paul Cézanne, Peintures, Aquarelles, Dessins,*, 1983, no. 5
London, Royal Academy of Arts, Paris, Musée d'Orsay; Washington, D.C., National Gallery of Art, *Cézanne, The Early Years 1859-1872*, 1988-1989, no. 35

Literature:
C. Borgmeyer, *The Master Impressionists*, Chicago, 1913, illustrated p. 272
Ambroise Vollard, *Paul Cézanne*, Paris, 1914, illustrated pl. 48
Evelyn Marie Stuart, "Cézanne and his place in Impressionism," *Fine Arts Journal* 35, no. 5 (May 1917), illustrated p. 338

Julius Meier-Graefe, *Cézanne und sein Kreis,*Munich, 1918, illustrated p. 87
(reprinted Munich, 1920, illustrated p. 87; Munich, 1922, illustrated p. 98)
Hans van Wedderkop, *Paul Cézanne*, Leipzig, 1922, illustrated
Georges Rivière, *Le Mâitre Paul Cézanne*, Paris, 1923, P. 196, illustrated p. 67
Roger Fry, "Le développement de Cézanne,"*Amour de L'Art*, Dec. 1926, illustrated p. 389
Roger Fry, *Cézanne: A study of His Development,* New York, 1927, pp. 15-16, illustrated pl. II
Julius Meier-Graefe, *Cézanne*, London, 1927, illustrated pl. IV
Kurt Pfister, *Cézanne, Gestalt, Werk, Mythos*, Potsdam, 1927, illustrated p. 101
Eugenio d'Ors, *Paul Cézanne*, Paris, 1930, illustrated p. 13 (In English, New York, 1936, illustrated pl. 37)
Georges Rivière, *Cézanne, Le peintre solitaire*, Paris, 1933, illustrated p. 5 (New edition, Paris, 1942, illustrated p. 7)
Beaux Arts, June 22, 1934, illustrated p. 6
M. Peschke-Koedt, "Der syvende Bud," *Samleren*, 1934, illustrated p. 6
Maurice Raynal, *Cézanne*, Paris, 1936, illustrated pl. V
Lionello Venturi, *Cézanne: Son Art, Son Oeuvre*, Paris, 1936, vol. I, p. 90, no. 105; vol. II, no. 105, illustrated pl. 27
Fritz Novotny, *Cézanne*, Vienna, 1937, illustrated pl. 8
G. di San Lazzaro, *Paul Cézanne*, Paris, 1938, illustrated fig. 37
Albert C. Barnes and Violette de Mazia, *The Art of Cézanne*, New York, 1939, no. 15, illustrated fig. 156
Raymond Cogniat, *Cézanne*, Paris, 1939, illustrated
Bernard Dorival, *Cézanne*, Paris, 1948, illustrated pl. 12
Gottard Jedlicka, *Cézanne*, Berne, 1948, illustrated fig. 5
Francis Jourdain, *Cézanne*, Paris and New York, 1950, illustrated
Lawrence Gowing, "Notes on the Development of Cézanne", *Burlington Magazine 98*, June 1956, pp. 185-192
Douglas Cooper, "Cézanne's Chronology" , *Burlington Magazine 98*, December 1956, p. 449
Robert Ratcliffe, *Cézanne's Working Methods and Their Theoretical Background*, (unpublished doctoral thesis, University of London, 1960)
Liliane Brion-Guerry, *Cézanne et l'expression de l'espace*, Paris, 1966, illustrated pl. 3
Frank Elgar, *Cézanne*, New York, 1975, illustrated fig. 10
Guila Ballar, "Paul Cézanne et la revue `L'Artiste,'" *Gazette des Beaux Arts*, n.s. 6, 98 (Dec. 1981), illustrated fig. 12
John Rewald, *Cézanne, A Biography*, New York, 1986, illustrated p. 51
Mary Louise Krumrine, *Paul Cézanne: The Bathers*, exhibition catalogue, Kunstmuseum Basel, 1989, illustrated pl. 22
Mary Thompkins Lewis, *Cézanne's Early Imagery,* Berkeley, 1989, pp. 68, 121-129, illustrated pl. VII
John Rewald, *The Paintings of Paul Cézanne, A Catalogue Raisonné*, London and New York, 1996, vol. I, p. 121, no. 142; vol. II, no. 142, illustrated p. 48

114 Paul Cézanne (1839-1906)

LA PROMENADE

Oil on canvas
11 by 14 ¼in. 28 by 36cm.

Painted *circa* 1866.

$500,000–700,000

Dated 1868-1870 (?) by Venturi (116), this painting has been assigned to 1866 by John Rewald. As he commented, "It is not surprising to note that during those years Cézanne's paintings are very diverse and often have little in common either in technique or composition. Besides large canvases, there are very small ones; besides scenes done completely from imagination, there are others for which Cézanne made use of studies sketched at the Atelier Suisse..." (John Rewald, *Paul Cézanne A Biography*, New York, 1948, pp. 80-81). This small study of two seated women and two standing men in contemporary dress would scarcely seem to have been conceived by the artist to whom the dark eroticism of *L'Enlèvement*, 1867 (Rewald 121) and the orgiastic splendour of *Le Festin (L'Orgie)*, also known as *Le Banquet de Nebuchadnezzar, circa* 1867 (Rewald 128) came so naturally, yet the totally dissimilar works were conceived within one year of each other. From the mid 1860s Cézanne was becoming increasingly interested in nature and was beginning to work outdoors, writing to Emile Zola on October 19 that he had discovered that nothing done in the studio would ever equal what was done outdoors. He was planning a large picture of his friends Antoine-Fortuné Marion and Antony Valabrègue ``setting out to look for a motif (a landscape motif of course)...the sketch, which Guillemet considers good and which I did after nature, makes everything else collapse and appear bad." (Quoted Gowing, 1988-89, p. 120). The sketch he was referring to- *Marion et Valabrègue partant pour le motif* (Rewald 99), also formerly in the Pellerin collection- is similar in subject and scale to *La Promenade* although in the latter it seems possible that he referred to a fashion plate in developing his composition. Whether or not this is the case, it is among the earliest surviving documents of Cézanne's desire to depict figures in the open air, albeit clothed and clearly his contemporaries.

This work is recorded in the Vollard Archives, photo. no. 587

Provenance:
Auguste Pellerin, Paris
Private collection

Exhibited:
Paris, Orangerie, *Hommage à Cézanne*, 1954, no. 16
London, Royal Academy of Arts; Paris, Musée d'Orsay; Washington, D.C., National Gallery of Art, *Cézanne, The Early Years 1859-1872*, 1988-1989, no. 26

Literature:
Georges Rivière, *Le Maître Paul Cézanne*, Paris, 1923, p. 201
Eugenio d'Ors, *Paul Cézanne*, 1930, illustrated pl. 30 (In English, *Paul Cézanne*, New York, 1936, illustrated pl. 33)
Georges Rivière , *Cézanne, le Peintre solitaire,* Paris, 1933, p. 108
Elie Faure, *Cézanne*, Paris, 1936, illustrated pl. 2
Maurice Raynal, *Cézanne*, Paris, 1936, illustrated pl. IX
Lionello Venturi, *Cézanne: Son Art, Son Oeuvre*, Paris, 1936, vol. I, p. 92, no. 116; vol. II, no. 116, illustrated pl. 28
G. di San Lazzaro, *Paul Cézanne*, Paris, 1938, illustrated fig. 43
Albert C. Barnes and Violette de Mazia, *The Art of Cézanne*, New York, 1939, no. 25, illustrated p. 164
Raymond Cogniat, *Cézanne*, Paris, 1939, illustrated pl. 4
Bernard Dorival, *Cézanne*, Paris, 1948, illustrated pl. 24
Douglas Cooper, "Cézanne's Chronology" , *Burlington Magazine 98*, December 1956, p. 449
Meyer Schapiro, *Cézanne*, Paris, 1973, illustrated p. 56
John Rewald, *The Paintings of Paul Cézanne, A Catalogue Raisonné*, London and New York, 1996, vol. I, p. 90, no. 87; vol. II, no. 87, illustrated p. 28

114

115 Paul Cézanne (1839-1906)

PARIS: QUAI DE BERCY- LA HALLE
AUX VINS

Oil on canvas
28 ¾ by 36 ¼ in. 73 by 92 cm.

Painted in 1872.

$3,000,000–4,000,000

Paul Cézanne (1839-1906), *La Maison du
Pendu, Auvers sur Oise,* 1873.
Musée d'Orsay, Paris.
© Photo RMN-Hervé Lewandowski

This is a view of the Halle aux Vins, a wine depot on the left bank of the Seine close to the Jardin des Plantes. Quoting a Parisian guidebook of 1803, Henri Loyrette described the depot as a "marketplace, which centralized the collection of duties on wines and eaux-de-vie," and which "occupied a large rectangular area defined by the quai Saint-Bernard, the rue-des-Fossés-Saint-Bernard, the rue de Jussieu and the rue Cavier, on which, since 1819, five large building complexes separated by avenues and divided into storerooms, (now the site of the Jussieu faculty) had been built" (Henri Loyrette in *Cézanne*, exhibition catalogue, Paris, London and Philadelphia, 1996, p. 131). Cézanne moved into an apartment on 45, rue Jussieu after December 1871 and painted this view in 1872. Starkly modern in feeling, it differs from the landscapes he was shortly to paint in Auvers not only in its leaden tonality, typical of a winter day in Paris, but also in the bold sweep of its composition defined by the plunging perspective of the ramp to the left. The following summer in Auvers in a work such as *La maison du pendu, Auvers-sur Oise* (Rewald 202- Musée d'Orsay, Paris), the surface is clotted and granular, the accumulation of brushstrokes evidence of the determination with which he attempted to convey his sensations before the motif, but in the present work it is the fluidity of his touch that impresses, for example in the balustrade that is conveyed in long uninterrupted strokes. If the mood is romantic and gloomy, it is no surprise since Cézanne's circumstances at the time were not the happiest. The apartment was cramped, his mistress Hortense Fiquet gave birth to a son, Paul, on January 4, 1872 and Cézanne himself was riddled with self-doubt. Achille Emperaire stayed with Cézanne briefly early in 1872 but not for long as he found his friend "pretty uncomfortable besides there being enough uproar to wake the dead." (Quoted in Rewald, p. 141), noise, perhaps from the baby as well as the wine depot across the street. Henri Loyrette has made the following observations: "This view, painted from a window in his apartment in the winter of 1872- one of the few works from this period that can be securely dated- has a palette altogether consistent with his despair: it is uniformly gray and brown, heightened very selectively with muted blues and reds in some of the wine kegs. It is dominated by the central row of dull trees, a sinister Parisian variation on the beautiful allée at the Jas de Bouffan. There is no sign here of noise or human presence (the distant buildings along the quai de Béthune are quite windowless) ...

115

We are far removed from the Parisian views of Monet and Renoir, so seductive and so teeming with life, that picture the city's historical center; we are rather closer to Jongkind, who had been painting the tortuous, ill-paved streets and ramshackle structures in the more eccentric neighborhoods of Paris for some time. But Jongkind, like Guillemet and, a bit later, Stanislas Lépine always made a few concessions to the picturesque sensibility. There are no such concessions in Cézanne's canvas, which is unique in his oeuvre, and which Pissarro, its first owner, impressed by its modest matter and the simplicity of its handling, praised for its 'vigor' and its 'remarkable force'." (Henri Loyrette in *Cézanne*, exhibition catalogue, Paris, London and Philadelphia, 1996, p. 131).

Pissarro's relationship with Cézanne was of profound importance to both artists. Totally dissimilar in temperament, the one calm and reflective, the other unruly and temperamental, they nevertheless succeeded in establishing a genuine rapport that was important on both a personal and artistic level. Pissarro saw Cézanne as "one of the most astonishing temperaments - the most remarkable of our age" (quoted in Christian Geelhar, ``The Painters who had the right eyes, on the reception of Cézanne's Bathers" in Mary Louise Krumrine's *Paul Cézanne The Bathers*, exhibition, Kunstmuseum Basel, 1989, p. 280). He admired *Paris: Quai de Bercy- La Halle aux Vins* even although it was the antithesis of everything he taught Cézanne while they painted together in Pontoise and Auvers-sur-Oise.

As a view of a specific site in modern Paris, the painting under discussion is unique in Cézanne's oeuvre although John Rewald pointed out that it belongs to a group of more or less monochromatic landscapes and still-lifes (Rewald, 1996 132-34, 136-38, and 157) and that this is the last. Its distinctiveness was not lost on Auguste Pellerin who also owned another remarkable view of Paris by Edouard Manet, *La rue mosnier aux drapeaux*, 1878 (Wildenstein 270).

Provenance:
Camille Pissarro, Paris
Auguste Pellerin, Paris
Private collection

Exhibited:
Paris, Orangerie, *Cézanne*, 1936, no. 22 (as *La Halle au Vin*)
Paris, Orangerie, *Hommage à Cézanne*, 1954, no. 22
London, Royal Academy of Arts; Paris, Musée d'Orsay; Washington, D.C.,
National Gallery of Art, *Cézanne, the Early Years 1854-1872*, 1988-1989, no. 62
Paris, Grand Palais; London, Tate Gallery; Philadelphia Museum of Art, *Cézanne*,
1995-1996, no. 26

Literature:
Roger Fry, "Le dévelopment de Cézanne," *Amour de l'Art*, Dec. 1926, illustrated
p. 396
Roger Fry, *Cézanne: A Study of His Development*, New York, 1927, pp. 22-23,
illustrated pl. VII, fig. 9
Georges Rivière, *Cézanne, Le Peintre Solitaire,* Paris, 1933, illustrated p. 57 (new
edition, Paris, 1942, illustrated p. 59)
Elie Faure, *Cézanne*, Paris, 1936, illustrated pl. 5
Lionello Venturi, *Cézanne:Son Art- Son Oeuvre*, Paris, 1936, vol. I, p. 78, no. 56;
vol. II, no. illustrated fig. 51
René Huyghe, "Cézanne et son oeuvre," *Amour de l'Art 17*, no. 5, May 1939,
illustrated fig. 51
John Rewald, "A propos du catalogue raisonné de l'oeuvre de Paul Cézanne et de la
chronologie de cette oeuvre," *La Renaissance 20*, (Mar.-Apr. 1937), illustrated p. 54
Fritz Novotny, *Cézanne*, Vienna, 1937, illustrated pl. 16
Fritz Novotny, *Cézanne und das Ende der Wissenschaftlichen Perspective*, Vienna,
1938, p. 206, no. 113, list of "motifs."
John Rewald, *Cézanne, Sa Vie, son oeuvre, son amitié pour Zola*, Paris, 1939, illus-
trated fig. 29
(In English: *Paul Cézanne, A Biography*, New York, 1948, illustrated fig. 37)
Raymond Cogniat, *Cézanne*, Paris, 1939, illustrated pl. 7
G. Bauer, *Paris-Peintres et écrivains*, Lausanne, 1944, p. 93
Bernard Dorival, *Cézanne*, Berne, 1948, illustrated pl. 30
Gotthard Jedlicka, *Cézanne*, Berne, 1948, illustrated fig. 10
Kenneth Clark, *Landscape Painting*, New York, 1950, pp. 121-122
Henri Perruchot, "Les Quinze Logis de Monsieur Cézanne," *L'Oeil*, Christmas
1955, pp. 33-34, illustrated
Douglas Cooper, "Cézanne's Chronology", *Burlington Magazine 98*, December
1956, p. 449
Robert Ratcliffe, "Cézanne's Working Methods and Their Theoretical
Background", (unpublished doctoral thesis, University of London, 1960)
Fritz Novotny, *Cézanne*, London, 1961, illustrated pl. 7
John Rewald, *Cézanne, A Biography*, New York, 1986, illustrated p. 94
John Rewald, *The Paintings of Paul Cézanne, A Catalogue Raisonné*, London and
New York, 1996, vol. I, pp. 141-142, no. 179; vol. II, no. 179, illustrated p. 62

Guide for Prospective Sellers

If you have property you wish to sell at auction, please call the appropriate specialist department to arrange for a consultation. (A list of specialist departments appears in the back of this catalogue.) If you are unsure which department would handle your property, or if you have a variety of objects to sell, please call one of our general representatives:

Fine Arts Representative, Nan Chisholm, (212) 606-7120

Inspection of Property

You may bring your property, or photographs if it is not portable, directly to our galleries where our specialists will give you auction estimates and advice. There is no charge for this service, but we request that you telephone ahead for an appointment. Inspection hours are 9:30 am to 5 pm, Monday through Friday.

Our specialists will provide a free preliminary auction estimate, subject to a final auction estimate after first-hand inspection, if you send a clear photograph of each item, or a representative group of photographs if you have a large collection. Please be sure to include the dimensions, artist's signature or maker's mark, medium, physical condition, and any other relevant information.

Evaluations of property can also be made at your home. The fees for such visits are based on the scope and diversity of the collection. Travel expenses are additional. These fees may be rebated if you consign your property for sale at Sotheby's.

Specialists from our Beverly Hills office are available for inspection visits in the western United States. For more information please call (310) 274-0340.

Standard Commission Rates

All private, trade and institutional sellers are required to pay a commission, which is based on the successful hammer price of property sold. For further details regarding specific commission rates, please refer to the cards that are available at our galleries, or contact the relevant specialist department. Other charges, including shipping, insurance, illustra-tion, restoration, unsold lots and minimum handling fees will be charged as applicable. (For more information about reserves, please refer to "Reserves" in the Guide to Prospective Buyers.)

Shipping Arrangements

Sotheby's Art Transport Department and the staff at any of our regional offices can assist you in making arrangements to have your property delivered to our galleries. This service is free, but actual packing, shipping and insurance charges are payable by our clients. (While we may recommend packers and shippers, we are not responsible for their acts or omissions.) For further information, please call Melanie Boehmer at (212) 606-7511.

Appraisals

Sotheby's Appraisal Company can prepare appraisals for insurance, estate tax, charitable contributions, family division or other purposes.

Appraisal fees vary according to the nature and amount of work to be undertaken, but will always be highly competitive. Flat rates can be quoted based on specialist time required, value and processing costs. Travel expenses are additional.

We shall be pleased to refund the appraisal fee pro rata if the appraised property is consigned to us for sale within one year after the appraisal is completed. For further information please call (212) 606-7440.

Financial Services

Sotheby's offers a wide range of financial services. These financial services include advances on consignments and loans secured by art collections which are not intended for sale. It is Sotheby's general policy, subject to exceptions, to lend no more than 40% of the total of its low estimates for such property. It is also Sotheby's general policy, subject to exceptions, that the minimum loan for consignor advances is $50,000, and the minimum loan for secured loans is $1,000,000. For further information regarding qualifications, conditions, and terms, please call Mitchell Zuckerman at (212) 606-7077.

Catalogues, Price Lists and *at Sotheby's*

Illustrated catalogues, prepared by Sotheby's specialists, are published for all regularly scheduled auctions and may be purchased singly or by annual subscription. (Catalogue subscribers automatically receive *at Sotheby's* at no additional charge.)

Printed lists of the prices realized at each auction are available at our galleries approximately three weeks following the auction, and are sent directly to catalogue purchasers and subscribers.

at Sotheby's, published seven times a year, provides an advance calendar of all Sotheby's sales worldwide and full-color photographs of auction highlights. A complimentary copy is available upon request. Annual subscriptions are $25 ($35 overseas).

For more information, or to subscribe to our catalogues or *at Sotheby's,* ask for our brochure. Write or call Sotheby's Subscription Department, P.O. Box 5111, Norwalk, CT 06856. Telephone: 1-800-444-3709.

Guide for Prospective Buyers

The following will help explain some of the words and symbols commonly used throughout this catalogue. All bidders should read the Conditions of Sale and Terms of Guarantee in this catalogue, as well as any Glossary or other notices. By bidding at auction, bidders are bound by those Conditions of Sale and Terms of Guarantee, as amended by any oral announcement or posted notices, which together form the contract of sale between the successful bidder (purchaser), Sotheby's and the seller (consignor) of the lot.

Symbol Key

This is a key that explains the symbols you may see inside this catalogue:

☐ *Reserves.* Lots with this symbol are subject to a reserve. A reserve is the confidential minimum price established between Sotheby's and the seller. This symbol will only be used if some, but not all, lots in the catalogue are offered subject to a reserve. If this symbol is not used, all lots in this catalogue are subject to a reserve.

○ *Guaranteed property.* Lots with this symbol indicate that Sotheby's has assured the seller a minimum price from one auction, or a series of auctions. This symbol will only be used if some, but not all, lots in the catalogue are offered subject to a guarantee.

△ *Property owned by Sotheby's.* Lots with this symbol indicate that Sotheby's owns the lot in whole or in part.

Please remember that all property is sold "As Is" and is only subject to rescission as stated in any applicable Terms of Guarantee. If you have any questions concerning the information below or any other auction practices, please contact Roberta Louckx at 606-7414.

Estimates

Each lot in the catalogue is given a low and high estimate. The estimates are guides for prospective bidders and, where possible, reflect prices that similar objects have sold for in the past. The estimates are determined several months before a sale and are therefore subject to revision to reflect current market conditions or currency fluctuations. Estimates should not be relied upon as a representation or prediction of actual selling prices. If you have any questions concerning a lot, please contact the specialist in charge of the sale whose name is printed in the front of the catalogue.

Specialist Advice; Exhibitions

Prospective bidders may be interested in specific information which is not included in the catalogue description of a lot. Do not hesitate to contact a Sotheby's specialist in a charge listed in the front of the catalogue, or Sotheby's Client Services Department, for additional information. A few days prior to every sale, there will be an exhibition of the property to be offered. Specialists will be available at the exhibition to answer questions about the property or to provide any other assistance with the auction process. The dates and times of the exhibition are printed in the front of this catalogue.

Bidding

In order to bid at an auction, you must qualify and register for a paddle when entering the salesroom. If you are the successful bidder on a lot, the auctioneer will acknowledge your paddle number. Unless you have previously qualified to bid at Sotheby's, please be prepared to provide requested information to a Sotheby's representative. This includes a form of identification i.e. Driver's license or Credit Card and, if you are bidding for someone else, you will need to provide a letter from that person, authorizing you to bid on that person's behalf. Issuance of a bid paddle is in Sotheby's sole discretion.

Bidding will be in accordance with the lot numbers listed in the catalogue or as announced by the auctioneer, and will be in increments determined by the auctioneer. There are three ways in which you may bid at auction. You may bid in person by attending the auction, submit an Absentee Bid Form, or in certain circumstances, by telephone. If you are unable to attend the sale, please see the Absentee Bid Form and Guide for Absentee Bidders which contains additional information on absentee bidding.

Unless otherwise noted in the catalogue or by an announcement at the auction, Sotheby's acts as agent on behalf of the seller and does not permit the seller to bid on his or her own property. It is important for all bidders to know that the auctioneer may open the bidding on any lot by placing a bid on behalf of the seller and may continue bidding for the seller by placing responsive or consecutive bids, but only up to the reserve (see the next paragraph below for information regarding reserves). The auctioneer will not place consecutive bids on behalf of the seller above the reserve.

Currency Conversion Board

For your convenience, in many sales Sotheby's operates a display board which converts United States dollars into various foreign currencies. All foreign currency amounts displayed are approximations based on recent exchange rate information and may not be relied upon as a precise invoice amount. Sotheby's assumes no responsibility for any error or omission in foreign or United States currency amounts shown.

Reserves

Unless otherwise indicated, all lots in this catalogue are offered subject to a reserve. A reserve is the confidential minimum price established between Sotheby's and the seller. The reserve is generally set at a percentage of the low estimate and will not exceed the low estimate of the lot. If any lots in the catalogue are offered without reserve, the lots subject to a reserve will be designated by a box (□).

Property in which Sotheby's has an interest

On occasions, Sotheby's offers property for sale and guarantees a minimum price to the consignor. Such property is also offered subject to a reserve and will be designated by the following symbol (○). Where every lot in a catalogue is guaranteed, Sotheby's will not designate each lot with the symbol, but will state in the Conditions of Sale page that every lot in the sale is subject to a guaranteed minimum price.

If Sotheby's owns property, in whole or in part, such property will be offered subject to a reserve and will be designated by the following symbol (△).

Hammer Price (or Successful Bid Price) and the Buyer's Premium

For lots which are sold, the last price for a lot as announced by the auctioneer is the hammer, or successful bid price. A buyer's premium will be added to the successful bid price and is payable by the purchaser as part of the total purchase price. The buyer's premium will be the amount stated in Paragraph 3 of the Conditions of Sale in the front of this catalogue.

Payment for Purchased Property

If you are the successful bidder on a lot, payment is to be made immediately following a sale. You will not be permitted to take delivery of your purchases until payment is made, unless a credit arrangement has been established. Please contact the specialist in charge of the sale, or Arlene Kick at (212) 606-7491, for information on a specific lot.

Payment for a lot may be made in United States dollars by cash, check, or coin transfer. Payment may also be made by Visa or MasterCard, subject to the following conditions.

Payment by Charge or Credit Card

If you wish to pay for any purchase with your MasterCard or Visa, you must present the card *in person* to Sotheby's. All charges are subject to acceptance by Sotheby's and by MasterCard or Visa, as the case may be. In the case a charge is not approved, you will nevertheless be liable to Sotheby's for all sums incurred by you. Credit card purchases may not exceed $25,000.

Payment by check

If you wish to pay by check, please see our cashier and fill out a Check Acceptance Account form. Until approved, you will not be permitted to remove purchases paid for by check until the check has cleared. Check Acceptance privileges are reviewed from time to time by Sotheby's, and may be granted or withdrawn in Sotheby's sole discretion. Checks drawn on foreign banks may not be accepted for values under $500, and credit card purchases may not exceed $25,000. There will be a collection charge minimum of $100 on checks drawn on foreign banks located outside of the continental United States.

Sales Tax

New York sales tax is charged on the successful bid price, buyer's premium and any other applicable charges on any property picked up or delivered in New York State, regardless of the state or country in which the purchaser resides or does business, unless Sotheby's has been given, in advance of the release of the property, a valid exemption from taxes by the State of New York. Sotheby's will also collect taxes on purchases shipped to California, Connecticut, Florida, Georgia, Illinois, Maryland, Massachusetts, Minnesota, New Jersey, Pennsylvania, Texas, Washington State and Washington, D.C. If you have any questions concerning this, please contact our Customer Billing Department at (212) 606-7444.

Removal of Property; Packing and Shipping

Unless otherwise agreed by Sotheby's, all purchases should be removed by the 10th day following a sale. Purchases which are not removed by the 10th day will be subject to a handling charge as outlined in paragraph 8 of the Conditions of Sale.

As a courtesy to purchasers who come to Sotheby's to pick up property, Sotheby's will assist in the packing of lots, although Sotheby's may, in the case of fragile articles, choose not to pack or otherwise handle a purchase. Sotheby's will not be responsible or liable for damage to glass covering paintings, drawings or other works, or damage to frames, regardless of the cause.

Sotheby's Art Transport Department and the staff at Sotheby's regional offices may be able to assist you in making arrangements for delivery and insuring of purchases. The purchaser will be responsible for shipping and insurance expenses. Sotheby's will also, upon request, provide names of professional packers and shippers known to the Art Transport Department, although Sotheby's shall have no liability or responsibility for providing this information. If you have any questions or wish further information, please contact the Art Transport Department at (212) 606-7511.

Export Permits

Certain property sold at auction may be subject to the provisions of the Endangered Species Act of 1973, the Marine Mammal Protection Act of 1972, the Migratory Bird Act of 1982 and the New York State Environmental Conservation Law. Although licenses can be obtained to export some items which are the subject of these laws, other items may not be exported (such as items containing whale bone), and some property may not be resold in the United States. Upon request, Sotheby's is willing to assist a purchaser in attempting to obtain appropriate licenses. However, there is no assurance that an export license can be obtained. Sotheby's will charge a minimum fee of $150 per item if it is able to obtain an export license. Please check with the specialist department or with the Art Transport Department if you are uncertain as to whether an item is affected by the above laws or other related laws which restrict exportation. The sale of a purchased lot will not be cancelled if Sotheby's, or a purchaser, is not able to obtain an export permit.

Absentee Bids

If you are unable to attend an auction in person, and wish to place bids, you may give Sotheby's Bid Department instructions to bid on your behalf. Our representatives will then try to purchase the lot or lots of your choice for the lowest price possible, and never for more than the top amount you indicate. This service is free and confidential. Please note: Sotheby's offers this service as a convenience to clients who are unable to attend the sale, and although we will make every effort, Sotheby's will not be responsible for error or failure to execute bids.

Placing Absentee Bids

To place bids, please use the absentee bid form provided in this catalogue. Be sure to accurately record the lot numbers and descriptions and the top price you are willing to pay for each lot. "Buy" or unlimited bids will not be accepted. Always indicate a "top limit"— the amount to which you would bid if you were attending the auction yourself.

Alternative bids should be indicated by using the word "OR" between lot numbers. Then if your bid on an early lot is successful, we will not continue to bid on other lots for you. Or, if your early bids are unsuccessful, we will continue to execute bids for alternative lots until a bid is successful. Bids must always be placed in the same order as the lot numbers appear in the catalogue.

Each absentee bid form should contain bids for one sale only; the number and code name should appear in the top right-hand corner of the form. Please place your bids as early as possible. In the event of identical bids, the earliest received will take precedence.

Telephone Bids

Bids may be placed by telephone, but are accepted only in Sotheby's discretion and at the caller's risk. In Sotheby's discretion, telephone bids may be recorded. By bidding on the telephone, prospective purchasers consent thereto.

Buyer's Premium

The "top limit" you indicate on your bid form is for the hammer price only. Please keep in mind that a buyer's premium will be added to the successful bid price of each lot you buy and is payable by you, together with the applicable sales tax which is applied to the total cost of your purchase (the total cost includes the buyer's premium). The buyer's premium will be the amount stated in paragraph 3 of the Conditions of Sale in the front of this catalogue.

Successful Bids

Successful bidders will be notified and invoiced within a few days of the sale. All bidders will receive a list of sale results if they purchased the sale catalogue or enclose a stamped self-addressed envelope with their absentee bid form.

For More Information

To place telephone bids, or for further information, please call Frederica Lauder at (212) 606-7414, or the regional office in your area.

Shipping/Forwarding Instructions

If your bid is successful, we can arrange to have your property shipped to you. As shipping costs can be expensive, we suggest that you request a quotation from our Art Transport Department at (212) 606-7511. If an estimate of shipping costs is not requested prior to shipment, we will act according to the instructions you provide. All shipments will be C.O.D.

The packing and shipping of items by Sotheby's employees is undertaken solely at our discretion. Furniture, larger items and high-valued property may require the services of professional packers.

Upon receipt of payment, Sotheby's will instruct packers and carriers. Your attention is drawn to the Conditions of Sale which require payment and clearance promptly after the sale. In default of those terms, lots may be transferred to a public warehouse at the risk and expense

of the purchaser. As stated in the Conditions of Sale, we are not responsible for the acts or omissions of carriers or packers, whether or not recommended by us. Packing and handling of purchased lots by us is at the entire risk of the purchaser.

Please allow 4 – 6 weeks for delivery.

Methods of Transport

Air Freight—Not to be confused with air mail, this method employs air freight carriers to ship property that has already been packed.

Registered Parcel Post—Parcels which do not exceed the size and weight limits set by the United States Postal Service may be sent by this method. In case of international shipments, it is not always possible to insure parcels for their full value. Please consult the Art Transport Department for details.

Truck—This method is recommended for large shipments and the transport of any item of furniture. There are also "shuttle services" which can transport uncrated paintings and works of art to specific areas in the United States. The Art Transport Department can supply complete details.

Book Post—This is a less expensive, but slower, method of shipping books via the United States Postal Service. Parcels shipped in this manner can be insured only for a maximum of $400.

For More Information

To receive an estimate of shipping costs, or for further information, please call Art Transport at (212) 606-7511, or the regional office in your area.

Absentee Bid Form

Sale Title   Ten paintings by Paul Cézanne

Date   November 13, 1997

Sale Code   "PELLERIN" 7075

Name *(please print or type)*   Date

Sotheby's Card #   Sotheby's Account #

Address

City   State   Zip Code

Telephone/Home   Business

Fax

☐ Please check if this is a new address.

Payment Note:

If you wish to pay for any purchase made by absentee bid with a Visa or Mastercard, you must present the card in person to Sotheby's.

Bank reference or deposit *(if bidder is unknown to Sotheby's)*

Bank Name   Account

Contact   Telephone

I agree that I am bound by the "Conditions of Sale" and any "Terms of Guarantee" which are published in the catalogue for the sale and govern all purchases at auction that I make.

Signed *(We must have your signature to execute this bid.)*

Sotheby's

1334 York Avenue
New York, N.Y. 10021
Bid Department (212) 606-7414

Important

Please see "Guide for Absentee Bidders" opposite this sheet.

I wish to place the following bids for this sale to be held on November 13, 1997. These bids are to be executed by Sotheby's up to but not exceeding the amount or amounts specified below. Each bid is PER LOT, as indicated, and all bids will be executed and are accepted subject to the "Conditions of Sale" and "Terms of Guarantee" printed in the catalogue of this sale. Please note that a buyer's premium in the amount stated in paragraph 3 of the "Conditions of Sale" in the front of this catalogue will be added to the hammer price as part of the total purchase price, plus any applicable sales tax.

Arranging Payment

In order to avoid delays in receiving purchases, buyers unknown to us are advised to make payment arrangements or supply credit references in advance of the sale date. If such arrangements are not made, purchases cannot leave our premises until checks have been cleared.

Please mail or fax to

Sotheby's Bid Department
1334 York Avenue
New York, N.Y. 10021
Fax (212) 606-7016

Lot Number	Catalogue/Description	Top Limit of Bid not including the buyer's premium
		$
		$
		$
		$
		$
		$
		$
		$
		$
		$

(please print or type)   *(Bid is per lot number as listed in the catalogue)*

AMERICAN DECORATIVE ARTS & FURNITURE
Leslie B. Keno — 606–7130
William W. Stahl, Jr. — 606–7110
John B. A. Nye — 606–7130
Wendell Garrett — 606–7137

AMERICAN FOLK ART
Nancy Druckman — 606–7225
Kara D. Short

AFRICAN & OCEANIC ART
Jean G. Fritts — 606–7325

AMERICAN INDIAN ART
Ellen Napiura Taubman — 606–7540

AMERICAN PAINTINGS, DRAWINGS & SCULPTURE
Peter B. Rathbone — 606–7280
Dara Mitchell

ANIMATION & COMIC ART
Dana Hawkes — 606–7910
Francie Ingersoll
Jerry Weist
Consultant

ANTIQUITIES
Richard M. Keresey — 606–7328
R. Seth Bright

ARMS & ARMOUR
Nicholas McCullough — 606–7260
Consultant

ART NOUVEAU & ART DECO
Barbara E. Deisroth — 606–7170
Gregory A. Kuharic
Frank Maraschiello

BOOKS & MANUSCRIPTS
David N. Redden — 606–7386
Dr. Paul Needham — 606–7385
Selby Kiffer
Marsha Malinowski
Justin E. Caldwell
Kimball E. Higgs
Elizabeth R. Muller

CANADIAN ART
Toronto
Christina Orobetz — (416) 926-1774

CHINESE PAINTINGS
Noah Kupferman — 606–7334
Andrew Wang

CHINESE WORKS OF ART
James B. Godfrey — 606–7332
Regina Krahl
Senior Consultant
Lark E. Mason, Jr.
Dr. Hugo K. Weihe
Dick Ning Wang

COINS AND MEDALS
Paul Song — 606–7856

COLLECTIBLES
Dana Hawkes — 606–7910

CONTEMPORARY PAINTINGS, DRAWINGS & SCULPTURE
Tobias Meyer — 606–7254
Leslie Prouty
Tracy Williams
Wendy Cromwell
Midwest
Helyn Goldenberg — (312) 664-6800
West Coast
Andrea Van de Kamp — (310) 274-0340

ENGLISH FURNITURE
Larry J. Sirolli — 606–7577
Peter Lang
Amanda Everard
William W. Stahl, Jr. — 606–7110

EUROPEAN FURNITURE
Phillips Hathaway — 606–7213
Gillian M. Arthur
Mary Frances Cunningham
Thierry Millerand

EUROPEAN WORKS OF ART & TAPESTRIES
Margaret H. Schwartz — 606–7250

FASHION
Tiffany Dubin — 774–5304

GARDEN STATUARY
Elaine Whitmire — 606–7285

IMPRESSIONIST & MODERN PAINTINGS, DRAWINGS AND SCULPTURE
Alexander Apsis — 606–7360
David Norman
Laurel Beckett
Scholarship and Research
John L. Tancock
Midwest
Helyn Goldenberg — (312) 664–6800
West Coast
Victoria Edwards — (310) 274–0340

INDIAN, HIMALAYAN, SOUTHEAST ASIAN WORKS OF ART & CONTEMPORARY INDIAN PAINTINGS
Carlton C. Rochell, Jr. — 606–7304

ISLAMIC WORKS OF ART
Richard M. Keresey — 606–7328
R. Seth Bright

JAPANESE ART
Ryoichi Iida — 606–7338
Gretchen Good

JEWELRY
John D. Block — 606–7392
Paul Russo
Gary Schuler
Antique
Jacqueline Fay
Business Development
Prince Dimitri of Yugoslavia
Tito Pedrini
Cataloguing and Research
Valerie Vlasaty
Arcade
Ann Limer Lange
Hilary Humphrey
West Coast
Tracy Sherman — (310) 786–1864
Carol Elkins
Midwest
Eve Reppen Rogers — (312) 664–6800
Canadian Sales
Michina Pope — (416) 926–1774
Gary Schuler — 606–7392

JUDAICA
Silver
Kevin L. Tierney — 606–7160
Books and Manuscripts
Dr. Paul Needham — 606–7385
Tel Aviv Liaison
Jennifer Roth — 606–7516

KOREAN WORKS OF ART
Ryoichi Iida — 606–7338
Jiyoung Koo — 606–7286

LATIN AMERICAN ART
Isabella Hutchinson — 606–7290
Cristina Vicinelli

MUSICAL INSTRUMENTS
Rachel Gaul — 606–7938

19TH CENTURY EUROPEAN PAINTINGS, DRAWINGS & SCULPTURE
Nancy Harrison — 606–7140
Benjamin F. Doller
Thomas Denzler
Claude Piening

Sculpture
Christopher Gow

19TH CENTURY FURNITURE, DECORATIONS & WORKS OF ART
Elaine Whitmire — 606–7285

OLD MASTER PAINTINGS & DRAWINGS
George Wachter — 606–7230
Heidi Chin
Christopher Apostle
Drawings
Scott Schaefer

PAPERWEIGHTS & GLASS
Lauren K. Tarshis — 606–7180

PHOTOGRAPHS
Denise Bethel — 606–7240
Christopher Mahoney

PORCELAIN: EUROPEAN & CHINESE EXPORT
Letitia Roberts — 606–7180

POSTAGE STAMPS
Robert A. G. A. Scott — 606–7915

PRE-COLUMBIAN ART
Stacy Goodman — 606–7330
Fatma Turkkan-Wille
Consultant

PRINTS (OLD MASTER AND MODERN)
Mary Bartow — 606–7117
Dr. Nancy Bialler
James Curtis

PRINTS (CONTEMPORARY)
Nina del Rio — 606–7113
Sharon Coplan

RUGS & CARPETS
Mary Jo Otsea — 606–7996

RUSSIAN ART, ICONS, OBJECTS OF VERTU
Gerard Hill — 606–7150

SILVER
Kevin L. Tierney — 606–7160
Ian Irving

SPORTS MEMORABILIA — 606–7910

VINTAGE CARS
David Patridge — 606–7920

WATCHES, CLOCKS & SCIENTIFIC INSTRUMENTS
Daryn Schnipper — 606–7162
Kevin L. Tierney — 606–7160

WINE
Serena Sutcliffe — 606–7207
Jamie Ritchie

SOTHEBY'S ARCADE AUCTIONS
Jennifer Roth — 606–7516
Decorations
Wiebke Moore — 606–7409
Victoria Ayers
Andrew Cheney
Susan Hunter
Paintings
Jennifer Roth — 606–7516
Helen Papoulias
Tiffany Thomas
Heather Galler-Brandes
Furniture
Constanze Doerr — 606–7588
Tim Hamilton
Beth Barnett
Jewelry
Ann Limer Lange — 606–7392
Hilary Humphrey
Rugs
Mary Jo Otsea — 606–7996
Emily Moqtaderi

24 HOUR SALE & EXHIBITION INFORMATION
606-7245

24 HOUR SALE RESULTS INFORMATION
606-7901

APPRAISALS
Lindsey Pryor — 606-7034

CATALOGUE SUBSCRIPTIONS
To order catalogues & price lists:
(800) 444-3709

Inquiries:
Diane Pia — (203) 849-4928

CLIENT SERVICES DIVISION
Bid Department
For assistance in placing absentee bids for North American Auctions.
606-7414

Romy Cohen
Lyn Grant
Frederica R. Lauder
Margot Moes
Kate Nelson
Courtney Ridenour
Ashley Riviere

Client Advisory Group
For information and assistance in all aspects of buying at auction in North America. Also assistance for non-English speaking clients.

Roberta Louckx	606-7415
Mallory Hathaway	606-7447
Lisa Heller	606-7468
Geraldine Nager Griffin	606-7568
Mish Tworkowski	606-7419
Brooke Douglass de Ocampo	606-7251
Brad Bentoff	606-7252

Client Service Exhibition Representative
Susan V. P. Barrett — 606-7087

Client Service Representative
Carole Bellidora — 606-7116

International Client Services
For information and assistance in all aspects of buying at auction outside of the U.S. Also assistance for non-English speaking clients.
Rose Balbo — 606-7400

Asian Client Relations
Jean Kim	606-7257
Natsuko Hidaka	606-7427

CLIENT ACCOUNTING
Arcade
Beverly Banks — 606-7147

Buyer Accounts
Arlene Kick — 606-7491

Seller Accounts
Cathy Jaque — 606-7320

CORPORATE COLLECTIONS
Naomi Baigell — 606-7575

FINANCIAL SERVICES
For Consignors & Collectors
Mitchell Zuckerman	606-7077
Shelley Fischer	606-7004

INTERNATIONAL CLIENT ADVISORY
Raul J. Suarez — 606-7274

MUSEUM SERVICES
Katherine Ross — 606-7303

RESTORATION:
FURNITURE & DECORATIONS
Colin Stair — 860-5446

SHIPPING &
CUSTOMS INQUIRIES
Melanie Boehmer — 606-7511

SPECIAL EVENTS
Margaret Race	606-7398
Mary Adickes	606-7374

SPECIAL SALES
Chapin Carson — 606-7446

SOTHEBY'S INSTITUTE
Kathleen Martin	606-7958
Elisabeth D. Garrett	606-7988
Jessica Deutsch	606-7838

TRUST & ESTATE SERVICES
Warren P. Weitman, Jr.	606-7198
Lindsey S. Pryor	606-7034
Christine Wheale	606-7445
Kathryn Wilmerding	606-7259
Deborah Schmidt	606-7090

New England
William S. Cottingham — (617) 247-2851

Middle Atlantic
Angela V. B. Hudson — (215) 751-9540

South
Robert Ruggiero — (704) 627-6001

Midwest
Laura MacLennan	(612) 332-8938
Deborah Schmidt	(212) 606-7090

Florida
David G. Ober — (407) 833-2582

West Coast
Sarah Blanchard — (310) 274-0340

ADMINISTRATIVE DEPARTMENTS

EXHIBITIONS
Alfred Bristol — 606-7460

FACILITIES & OPERATIONS
Wendell Walker	606-7232
Conrad Webb	606-7547

FINANCE & ADMINISTRATION
Jerry Kasdan	606-7820
Karen Schuster	606-7410
Gail Skelly	606-7399
Margaret Race	606-7398

FINANCIAL OPERATIONS
Tricia Carberry	774-5337
Elsie Spencer	606-7410

HUMAN RESOURCES
Susan Alexander	606-7204
Daryl Krimsky	606-7202
Anne-Marie DeGeorge	606-7075

INFORMATION SYSTEMS
Paul Cuccia	606-7807
Winston Poyser	606-7881
Jag Jagtiani	606-7821

INVESTOR RELATIONS
Jeff Pierne — 606-7390

LEGAL
Rena J. Moulopolous	606-7175
Allison Corey Miller	
Miori Tsubota	
Daryl Wickstrom	

MARKETING
Suzanne McMillan	606-7354
Richard Buckley	606-7527
Emil T. Micha	606-7273
Tove Nedergaard	606-7539
Ronald Varney	606-7189

PHOTOGRAPHY
Ben Cohen — 606-7210

PRESS OFFICE /
CORPORATE AFFAIRS
Diana Phillips	606-7176
Matthew Weigman	

REGIONAL OPERATIONS
Wendy Armacost — 606-7442

TREASURY
John Brittain	606-7220
Jeff Pierne	606-7390

CREDITS

PRODUCTION COORDINATOR
Tara Theune

PHOTOGRAPHERS
David Hays
Bonnie Morrison

COVER DESIGN
Emil Micha

LAYOUT AND DESIGN
Ethan Crenson

PRINTING
Centennial Printing Corp.

SEPARATOR
Toppan Printing Co. of America

2/97

United Kingdom and Ireland
London
34–35 New Bond Street
and Bloomfield Place
(off New Bond Street)
London W1A 2AA
Telephone: (0171) 493 8080
Fax: (0171) 409 3100

SOUTH EAST
Sale Room
Michael Thomson-Glover
Alistair Morris
Summers Place, Billingshurst
West Sussex RH149AD
Telephone: (1403) 783 933
Telex: 87210 GAVEL
Fax: (1403) 785 153

Kent and East Sussex
The Hon. George Plumptre
Ashford, Kent
Telephone: (1233) 620773
Fax: (1233) 632652

Richard Eyton-Lloyd
Seaford, East Sussex
Telephone: (1323) 894520

Home Counties
John Hudson
Telephone: (171) 408 5897

HAMPSHIRE
Julian and Carolyn Sheffield
Spring Pond, Laverstoke Lane
Whitchurch
Hampshire RG28 7PD
Telephone: (1256) 895447
Fax: (1256) 895449

WALES AND SOUTH WEST
John Harvey
18 Imperial Square
Cheltenham
Gloucestershire GL50 1QZ
Telephone: (1242) 510500
Fax: (1242) 250252
The Hon. Mrs. d'Erlanger
Tiverton, Devon
Telephone: (1884) 243663
Fax: (1884) 258692

Wessex
Colin Thompson
Cheviot House
69–73 Castle Street
Salisbury, Wiltshire SP1 3SP
Telephone: (1722) 330793
Fax: (1722) 330982

Northhamptonshire
Mary Miller
Towcester, Northhamptonshire
Telephone: (1327) 860020
Fax: (1327) 860612

East Midlands
The George Hotel Mews
Station Road, Stamford
Lincolnshire PE9 2LB
Telephone: (1780) 51666
Fax: (12780) 62086

East Anglia
Chantal Langely
Cleveland House
39 Old Station Road
Newmarket, Suffolk CB8 8DT
Telephone: (1638) 561426
Fax: (1638) 560094

The Lord Cranworth
Woodbridge, Suffolk
Telephone: (1473) 735581
Fax: (1473) 738278
Sara Foster
Fakenham, Norfolk
Telephone: (1328) 700032
Fax: (1328) 700155

NORTH WEST
Timothy Wonnacott, A.R.I.C.S.
Summer Hill
168 Chester Road
Macclesfield
Cheshire, SK11 8PT
Telephone: (1244) 315531
Fax: (1244) 346984

Lord Ralph Kerr
Melborne, Derbyshire
Telephone/Fax: (1332) 862263

YORKSHIRE
John Phillips
William Sheepshanks
8–12 Montpellier Parade
Harrogate
North Yorkshire HG1 2TJ
Telephone: (1423) 501466
Fax: (1423) 520501

SCOTLAND AND BORDER COUNTIES
John Robertson
Nicholas Linzec Gordon
112 George Street
Edinburgh EH2 4LH
Telephone: (131) 226 7201
Fax: (131) 226 6866

Anthony Weld Forester
130 Douglas Street
Glasgow G2 4HF
Telephone: (141) 221 4817
Fax: (141) 204 2502

Nicholas Linzec Gordon
Aberdeenshire
Telephone: (1330) 824007

NORTHERN ENGLAND
Matthew Festing
11 Osborne Terrace, Jesmond
Newcastle-upon-Tyne
NE2 1NE
Telephone: (191) 281 8867
Fax: (191) 212 0141

Judith Heelis
Appleby, Cumbria
Telephone/Fax: (17683) 52806

NORTHERN IRELAND
William Montgomery
The Estate Office, Grey Abbey
Newtownards, Co. Down
Telephone: (124 77) 88 666/8
Fax: (124 77) 88 652

IRELAND
Anne Dillon
William Montgomery
51b Dawson Street, Dublin 2
Telephone: 353 (1) 671 1786
and 353 (1) 671 1431
Fax: 353 (1) 679 7844

CHANNEL ISLANDS
Bailiwick of Guernsey
Telephone: (1481) 715415
Fax: (1481) 714511

Clare d'Abo
Jersey
Telephone: (171) 408 5363

Europe and Middle East
AUSTRIA
Dr. Agnes Husslein
Managing Director–Austria & Hungary
Vienna
Tel: 43 (1) 512 4772/3 and
513 3774
Fax: 43 (1) 513 4867

Vienna
Dr. Agnes Husslein
Palais Breuner
Singerstrasse 16, 1010 Vienna

Tel: 43 (1) 512 4772/3 and
513 3774
Fax: 43(1) 513 4867

Graz
Dr. Soraya Stubenberg
Schloss Gutenberg, A-8160 Weiz
Telephone: 43 (3172) 8133
Fax: 43 (3172) 8133 12

Klagenfurt
Villacher Strasse 813
A-9020
Telephone: 43 (463) 50 44 84
Fax: 43 (463) 50 44 82

BELGIUM
Count Hubert d'Ursel
Managing Director
Monique Bréhier
32 Rue Jacques Jordaens
1050 Brussels
Telephone: 32 (2) 648 0080
Fax: 32 (2) 648 0757

CYPRUS
Rita C. Severis
15 Them Dervis Str.
P.O. Box 1139, Nicosia, Cyprus
Telephone: 357 (2) 461410
Fax: 357 (2) 361716

CZECH REPUBLIC
Dr. Katharina Prinzessin
Zu Sayn-Wittgenstein
Celetna 10
110 00 Prague 1
Tel/Fax: 42 (20) 232 2839

DENMARK
Baroness Hanne Wedell-Wedellsborg
Bredgade 6
1260 Copenhagen K, Denmark
Telephone: 45 (33) 135556
Fax: 45 (33) 930119

FINLAND
Claire Svartstrom
Fabianinkatu 14A
00100 Helsinki
Telephone: 358 (0) 62 21 558
Fax: 358 (0) 68 01 208

FRANCE
Paris
Princess de Beauvau Craon
(*P.D.G., France*)
Kristen van Riel
Managing Director, France
Alexandre Pradere
Francis Simon
Anne de Lacretelle
Associate
Prince Abdel 'Azis Toussoun
Associate
3 rue de Miromesnil
75008 Paris
Telephone: 33 (1) 53 05 53 05
Telex: SPBF A 640084 F
Fax: 33 (1) 474 222 32

Bordeaux
France de Sainte Croix
Telephone: 33 56 44 95 23
Fax: 33 56 01 09 26

Montpellier
Beatrice Viennet
Telephone: 33 67 24 95 72
Fax: 33 67 24 93 52

Strasbourg
Marie-France Ludmann
Telephone: 33 88 60 00 61
Fax: 33 88 60 00 61

GERMANY
Heinrich Graf von Spreti
Managing Director
Munich
Telephone: 49 (89) 2913151

Frankfurt
Johannes Ernst
Nina Buhne
Mendelssohnstrasse 66
60325 Frankfurt Main
Telephone: 069 74 0787
Fax: 49 (69) 746 901

Berlin
Isabella von Bethmann-Hollweg
Lucy Dew
Palais am Festungsgraben
Unter den Linden/Neue Wache
D-10117 Berlin
Telephone: 49 (30) 204 4119
Fax: 49 (30) 394 3080

Cologne
Ursula Niggemann
St. Apern-Strasse 17–21
D-50667 Cologne
Telephone: 49 (221) 257 4956/7
or 257 4972
Fax: 49 (221) 257 4359

Hamburg
Tatiana von Hessen
Axel Benz
Innocentiastrasse 19
D-20149 Hamburg
Telephone: 49 (40) 44 40 80
Fax: 49 (40) 410 7082

Munich
Heinrich Graf von Spreti
Andreas Narzt
Odeonsplatz 16
D-80539 München 22
Telephone: 49 (89) 291 31 51
Fax: 49 (89) 299 271

Lower Saxony
Susanne von Luneburg
Rittergut Essenrode
D-38165 Essenrode
Telephone: 49 (5301) 1366
Fax: 49 (5301) 1227

Stuttgart
Heide Rentschler
Bodenseestrasse 23
88138 Sigmarszell
Telephone: 49 (8389) 323
Fax: 49 (8389) 32707

Karlsruhe
Cornelia von Griesheim
Geigersbergsstrasse 22
D-76185 Karlsruhe
Telephone: 49 (721) 941 5200
Fax: 49 (721) 941 5201

GREECE
Rita C. Severis
15 Them Dervis Str.
P.O. Box 1139, Nicosia, Cyprus
Telephone: 357 (2) 461 410
Fax: 357 (2) 444 897

HOLLAND
John van Schaik
102 Rokin, 1012 KZ Amsterdam
Telephone: 31 (20) 550 2200
Telex: 13267 MAKSO NL
Fax: 31 (20) 550 2222

HUNGARY
Dr. Soraya Stubenberg
Attila utca 111/4th Floor/1
H-1012 Budapest
Telephone: 36 (1) 175 2961
Fax: 43 (3172) 8133 12

ICELAND
Sigridur Ingvarsdottir
1 Hofsvallagata, 101 Reykjavik
Telephone: 354 (1) 204 37
Fax: 354 (1) 62 04 37

ISRAEL
Rivka Saker Managing Director
Daniella Luxembourg
38 Gordon Street
Tel Aviv 63414
Telephone: 972 (3) 522 3822 or
524 6897
Fax: 972 (3) 522 5454

ITALY
Giuseppe Ceccatelli
Managing Director

Milan
Giuseppe Ceccatelli
Palazzo Broggi
Via Broggi 19
20129 Milan
Telephone: 39 (2) 295001
Fax: 39 (2) 29518595

Rome
Julien Stock
Piazza di Spagna 90
00187 Rome
Telephone: 39 (6) 699 41791
or 678 1798
Fax: 39 (6) 679 6167

Florence
Clementina Bartolini Salimbeni
Telephone: 39 (55) 247 9021
Fax: 39 (55) 247 9563

Turin
Laura Russo
Corso Galileo, Ferraris 18B
10121 Turin
Telephone: 39 (11) 544898
Fax: 39 (11) 547675

LIECHTENSTEIN
Henriette Huber-von
Goldschmidt Rothschild
Josef Rheinbergerstr, 11A
FL9490 Vaduz
Telephone: 41 (75) 232 4914
Fax: 41 (75) 233 1738

LUXEMBOURG
Nadia Meyer-Quiring
156A Route de Luxembourg
L-7374 Bofferdange
Telephone: 352 33 97 47
Fax: 353 33 51 60

MONACO
Alain Renner
Mark Armstrong
B.P. 45, Le Sporting d'Hiver
Place du Casino
MC 98001 Monaco Cedex
Telephone: 377 (93) 30 88 80
Fax: 377 (93) 25 24 98

NORWAY
Ingeborg Astrup
Bjornveien 42
0387 Oslo 3, Norway
Telephone: 47 (22) 14 72 82
Fax: 47 (22) 49 38 36

PORTUGAL
Frederico Horta e Costa
Calcada do Combro, 38A - 1
1200 Lisbon
Telephone: 351 (1) 343 1041
Fax: 351 (1) 342 6536

SPAIN
Madrid
Carmen Araoz de Urquijo
Chairman, Sotheby's Spain
Jose de Paz de la Brena
Managing Director
Plaza de la Independencia 8
28001 Madrid
Telephone: 34 (1) 522 2902
Fax: 34 (1) 521 4482

Barcelona
Rocio Tassara
Luis Monreal Tejada
Associate
Pasaje de Domingo 2
08004 Barcelona
Telephone: 34 (3) 487 6845/5272
Fax: 34 (3) 216 0792

Bilbao
Ines Barrenechea
Diputation 8
48008 Bilbao
Tel/Fax: 34 (4) 479 0946

SWEDEN
Hans Dyhlen
Arsenalsgatan 6
111 47 Stockholm
Telephone: 46 (8) 679 5478/9
Fax: 46 (8) 611 4826

Gothenburg
Vivianne Kempe
Telephone: 46 (31) 937 150
Fax: 46 (31) 937 550

South Sweden
Baroness Catharina von Blixen-
Finecke
Telephone: 46 (411) 85130
Fax: 46 (411) 85128

SWITZERLAND
Simon de Pury
Chairman–Europe
Geneva
Telephone: 41 (22) 732 8585

Geneva
Simon de Pury
David Bennett
Daniella Luxembourg
13 Quai du Mont Blanc
CH-1201 Geneva
Telephone: 41 (22) 908 4800
Fax: 41 (22) 908 4804

Zurich
Daniella Luxembourg
20 Bleicherweg, CH-8002 Zurich
Telephone: 41 (1) 202 0011
Fax: 41 (1) 201 2042

Lugano
Diego Cassina
Via Peri 21, 6900 Lugano
Telephone: 41 (91) 9238562
Fax: 41 (91) 9238563

Basel
Ruedi Staechelin
Schifflande 2
CH-4051 Basel
Telephone: 41 (61) 261 10 20
Fax: 41 (61) 261 10 77

SYRIA AND JORDAN
Antoine Touma
P.O. Box 2011
Damascus, Syria
Telephone: 963 (11) 429 502

....

Asia

CHINA
Wang Jie
Dynasty Business Centre,
Room 401
457 Wu Lu Mu Qi Road (N)
Shanghai 20040, PRC
Telephone: 86 (21) 6249 7450
Fax: 86 (21) 6249 7451

HONG KONG
Alice Lam
Co-Chairman, Asia
Lisa Hubbard
Director,
International Jewelry, Asia

Li Po Chun Chambers
18th Floor
189 Des Voeux Road
Central, Hong Kong
Telephone: (852) 2 524 8121
Fax: (852) 2 810 6238

INDIA
Javed Abdulla
113 Sunder Nager
New Delhi 110003
Tel and fax: 91 11 463 8385

Dr. Usha Ramamrutham
12 Juhu Ajanta
Gulmohar Road
J.V.P.D. Scheme
Bombay 400 049
Tel and fax: 91 (22) 620 2321

Patrick Bowring (London)
Telephone: 071 408 5407

INDONESIA
Martina Sudwikatmono
Subentra Building, 8th Floor
Jl. Gatot Subroto, Kav. 21
Jakarta 12930
Indonesia
Telephone: 62 (21) 522-0156
Fax: 62 (21) 522-0074

JAPAN
Tetsuji Shibayama
Managing Director
Fuerte Kojimachi Bldg. 3F
1–7 Kojimachi
Chiyoda-ku, Tokyo 102
Telephone: 81 (3) 3230 2755
Fax: 81 (3) 3230 2754

KOREA
Howard Rutkowski
2F, 192–11 Kwanhoon-Dong
Jongro-Gu, Seoul
Korea 110–300
Telephone: 82 (2) 733 5733
Fax: 82 (2) 733 4733

MALAYSIA
Walter Cheah
25 Jalan Pudu Lama
50200 Kuala Lumpur
Telephone: 60 (3) 230 0319
Fax: 60 (3) 230 6833

SINGAPORE
Quek Chin Yeow
1 Cuscaden Road
01–01 The Regent Singapore
Singapore 1024
Telephone: (65) 732 8239
Fax: (65) 737 0295

TAIWAN R.O.C.
Rita Wong
1st Floor, No. 79
Sec. 1, An Ho Road
Taipei, Taiwan R.O.C.
Telephone: 886 (2) 755 2906 or
704 6002/3
Fax: 886 (2) 709 3949

THAILAND
Geoffrey Longfellow
6th Floor, Rajapark Building
163 Asoke Road
Sukhumvit 21
Bagkok 10110, Thailand
Telephone: 66(2) 611 1064
Fax: (662) 258 9038

AUSTRALIA
Sydney
Robert Bleakley
Chairman
Justin Miller

Level 1
118-122 Queen Street
Woollahra, NSW, 2025
Telephone: 61 (2) 9 362 1000
Fax: 61 (2) 9 362 1100

Melbourne
Paul Sumner
926 High Street, Armadale
Melbourne, Victoria 3143
Telephone: 61 (3) 9 509 2900
Fax: 61 (3) 9 563 5067

....

Latin America

ARGENTINA
Adela MacKinlay de Casal
Consultant
Avenida Callao 1777 (P.B.)
1024 Buenos Aires
Telephone: (541) 811 2965
(541) 813 2159
Fax: (541) 814 5033

BRAZIL
Rio de Janeiro
Katia Mindlin Leite Barbosa
Consultant
Caixa Postal 62619
Rio de Janeiro, RJ CEP 22250-970
Telephone: 55 (21) 551 6775
Fax: 55 (21) 551 5899

Heloise Guinle
Consultant
Estrada da Gavea 611
Bloco 1, Apt 2503, São Conrado
22610-000 Gavea
Rio de Janeiro
Telephone: 55 (21) 322 4500
Fax: 55 (21) 322 6397

São Paulo
Pedro Corrêa do Lago
Consultant
Rua João Cachoeira 267
São Paulo SP CEP 04535-010
Telephone: 55 (11) 282 0066
Fax: 55 (11) 282 6559

MEXICO
Mexico City
Françoise Reynaud de Velez
Consultant
Suzy de Gilly
Consultant
Kepler 189
Mexico 11590 D.F.
Telephone: (525) 531 0595
Fax: (525) 545 6971

Gonzalo Gonzalez
Consultant
Schiller 325-7, Polanco
Mexico 11570 D.F.
Telephone: (525) 531 1686/1806
Fax: (525) 250 8734

Monterrey
Barbara Perusquia de Lobeira
Consultant
Via Triumphalis 127 PTE.
Fuentes Del Valle
Monterrey 66220, N.L.
Telephone: (528) 356 9209
Fax: (528) 378 2432

VENEZUELA
Axel Stein
Consultant
C. C. C. T. Primera Etapa
Piso 3 Of. 312
Chuao, Caracas 1060
Telephone: (582) 959 2249
Fax: (582) 959 1832

Headquarters
1334 York Avenue
New York, New York 10021
Telephone: (212) 606–7000
Fax: (212) 606–7107
(212) 606–7016 (Bids only)

Offices and Associates
U.S.A.
Atlanta
Virginia Groves Beach
Associate of Sotheby's
2300 Peachtree Road, NW
Suite 205B
Atlanta, Georgia 30309
Telephone: (404) 355–7225
Fax: (404) 355–8599
Baltimore
Aurelia Bolton
Associate of Sotheby's
P.O. Box 250
Riderwood, Maryland 21139
Telephone: (410) 252–4600
Fax: (410) 561–9738
Beverly Hills
9665 Wilshire Blvd.
Beverly Hills, California 90212
Telephone: (310) 274–0340
Fax: (310) 274–0899
Andrea L. Van de Kamp
Chairman, West Coast
Richard S. Wolf
Managing Director, West Coast
Sarah Blanchard
Trusts & Estates
Tracy Sherman
Carol Elkins
Jewelry
Victoria Edwards
Fine Arts
Katherine Watkins
Decorative Arts
Eleanore Phillips Colt
Associate of Sotheby's
Christine Eisenberg
Associate of Sotheby's
Nancy O. Livingston
Associate of Sotheby's
Chicago
215 West Ohio Street
Chicago, Illinois 60610
Telephone: (312) 670–0010
Fax: (312) 670–4248
Helyn D. Goldenberg
Chairman, Midwest
Jamie Ritchie
Managing Director
Leslie Hindman
Business Development
Eve Reppen Rogers
Jewelry
Cassie Spencer
Trusts & Estates
Robert Tilendis
Administrator
Marjorie S. Susman
Associate of Sotheby's
Dallas
Nancy Strauss Halbreich
Associate of Sotheby's
8409 Pickwick Lane, #284
Dallas, Texas 75225–5323
Telephone: (214) 265–9958
Fax: (214) 369–0332

Honolulu
Andrea Song Gelber
Associate of Sotheby's
P.O. Box 177
Honolulu, Hawaii 96810
Telephone: (808) 732–0122
Fax: (808) 732–0122
Houston
Laura H. Morris
Associate of Sotheby's
Windi Phillips
2476 Bolsover, Suite 143
Houston, Texas 77005
Telephone: (713) 524–0044
Fax: (713) 520–1602
Long Island
Kim Coleman
Associate of Sotheby's
3–1 Park Plaza, Suite 170
Old Brookville, New York
11545
Telephone: (516) 621–7240
Fax: (516) 625–2919
Miami
Stefanie Block Reed
Dolores C. Smithies
Consultant
Douglas Entrance
800 Douglas Road, Suite 125
Coral Gables, Florida 33134
Telephone: (305) 448–7882
Fax: (305) 448–7168
Minneapolis/St. Paul
Laura MacLennan
2030 Foshay Tower
821 Marquette Avenue
Minneapolis, Minnesota 55402
Telephone: (612) 332–8938
Fax: (612) 332–7456
Naples
Barbara Deisroth
Telephone: (813) 261–6787
Fax: (813) 263–5860
New England
William S. Cottingham
Managing Director
Patricia Ward
Representative
67 1/2 Chestnut St.
Boston, Massachusetts 02108
Telephone: (617) 367-6323
Fax: (617) 367-4888
New Orleans
Debe Cuevas Lykes
Associate of Sotheby's
Telephone: (504) 523–7059
North Carolina
Robert V. Ruggiero
Consultant
598 Fog Hollow Cove
Clyde, North Carolina 28721
Telephone: (704) 627–6001
Fax: (704) 627–2059
New York City/Southampton
Barbara D. Cates
Associate of Sotheby's
1334 York Avenue
New York, New York 10021
Telephone: (212) 644–5310
Fax: (704) 644–0468
Palm Beach
225 Peruvian Avenue
Palm Beach, Florida 33480
Telephone: (561) 833–2582
Fax: (561) 655–4583

David G. Ober
Managing Director, Florida
Susan Sencer
Administrator
Hope P. Kent
Associate of Sotheby's
Louis J. Gartner
Associate of Sotheby's
Kim Coleman
Associate of Sotheby's
Philadelphia
Wendy T. Foulke
Angela Hudson
Trusts & Estates
1831 Chestnut Street, Suite 601
Philadelphia, Pennsylvania
19103
Telephone: (215) 751–9540 or
(215) 751–9349
Fax: (215) 751–0936
Puerto Rico
Marta Gutierrez
Associate of Sotheby's
7061 Carretera 187, Apt. 1401
Carolina, Puerto Rico 00908
Telephone: (787) 791–1971
Fax: (787) 791–6591
St. Louis
Marjorie S. Susman
Associate of Sotheby's
Telephone: (314) 991–4939
San Francisco
Jennifer Seymour Foley
Mrs. Prentis Cobb Hale
Associate of Sotheby's
Mrs. John N. Rosekrans
International Representative
214 Grant Avenue, Suite 350
San Francisco, California 94108
Telephone: (415) 772–9028
Fax: (415) 772–9031
Santa Fe
Windi Phillips
Associate of Sotheby's
Telephone: (713) 524–0044
Fax: (713) 520-1602
Seattle
Jeannie Johnston
P.O. Box 4356
Seattle, Washington 98104
Telephone: (206) 667-9575
Fax: (206) 667-9576
Tampa
Debe Cuevas Lykes
Associate of Sotheby's
P.O. Box 13782
Tampa, FL 33681–3782
Telephone: (813) 832–4741
Fax: (813) 832–4542
Washington, D.C.
Sally E. Chapoton
Associate of Sotheby's
2201 Wisconsin Avenue, N.W.,
Suite 390
Washington, D.C. 20007
Telephone: (202) 457–1910
Fax: (202) 457–8100
BERMUDA
William S. Cottingham
c/o Cooper Associates
P.O. Box WK 99
Warwick WK BX Bermuda
Telephone: (809) 295–6891
Fax: (809) 295-7392

CANADA
Christina Orobetz
President
Brian Watson
Vice President
9 Hazelton Avenue
Toronto, Ontario M5R 2E1
Telephone: (416) 926–1774
Fax: (416) 926–9179
Kenzie Selman
Associate of Sotheby's
2365-232 Street
Langley, B.C. V6K 6H5
Telephone: (604) 533–8232
Fax: (604) 732-6501
Gillian Stewart
Associate of Sotheby's
3230 Beach Drive
Victoria, B.C. V8R 6L8
Telephone: (250) 370–1021
Fax: (250) 592–2884

Sotheby's International Realty
President
Stuart N. Siegel
980 Madison Avenue
New York, New York 10021
Telephone: (212) 606–4100
Fax: (212) 606–4199

Sotheby's Appraisal Company
(Insurance and Estate Appraisals)
Director
Lindsey Pryor
1334 York Avenue
New York, New York 10021
Telephone: (212) 606–7034
Fax: (212) 606–7022

Sotheby's Restoration
(Furniture)
Director
Colin Stair
1425 York Avenue
New York, New York 10021
Telephone: (212) 860–5446
Fax: (212) 876–1064

Sotheby's Financial Services, Inc.
Mitchell Zuckerman
President
Shelley Fischer
Vice President
1334 York Avenue
New York, New York 10021
Telephone: (212) 606–7077
Fax: (212) 606–7023

International Representatives
Marion Oates Charles
Newport, Washington D.C.
Nancy Strauss Halbreich
Dallas
Windi Phillips
Houston, Santa Fe
Mrs. John N. Rosekrans
San Francisco
Marjorie S. Susman
Chicago, St. Louis
Lee Copley Thaw
New York City
Virginia Guest Valentine
New York City, Richmond
Telephone: (212) 606–7442
Fax: (212) 606–7022